The Bloodstream:
River of Life

The Bloodstream

RIVER OF LIFE

ISAAC ASIMOV

William J. Mehm

COLLIER BOOKS

NEW YORK

COLLIER MACMILLAN PUBLISHERS

LONDON

First Collier Books Edition 1961
Fifth Printing 1973
The Bloodstream *was originally published in the United States in
1959 under the title* The Living River
This Collier Books edition is published by arrangement with
Abelard-Schuman Limited
Macmillan Publishing Co., Inc.
Collier-Macmillan Canada Ltd.

PRINTED IN UNITED STATES OF AMERICA

Contents

The Bloodstream:
River of Life

Chapter 1

A Pinch of Ocean

ANY ONE-CELLED CREATURE in the sea, a creature so small a microscope is needed to see it, has a blood supply billions upon billions of times as large as our own.

This may sound impossible until you realize that for that one-celled creature the entire ocean is a kind of blood supply. The one-celled creature absorbs food and oxygen from the ocean, as our tissues do from blood. It discharges its waste products into the ocean, as our tissues do into blood.

And probably that is how life first developed: as a microscopic blob of living substance dining lazily on an ocean crowded with edible compounds that had slowly been built up out of simple compounds by the ultraviolet light of the sun. It was only as life multiplied and the food supply diminished that a premium was placed on more efficient methods of getting along. Primitive life was thrust out of its Eden, so to speak, and had to learn to work for a living.

One method of increasing efficiency was for cells to band together in a cooperative community, somewhat as primitive human beings might band together to form a tribe or village. The cells would specialize; some being particularly designed to hold the whole organism firmly in place on a rock, let us say, others to absorb food and so on.

But even in the most complicated ocean plants, the seaweeds, specialization has not gone very far. Although the individual seaweed may be a sizable organism, it is made up of

11

thin, branching strands so that the cells of which it is composed are all bathed by the ocean or, at the very least, are blocked off from the ocean by so few other cells that food and oxygen can still penetrate to all of them.

Even today, ocean plants have a pretty lazy life. Given sunlight, carbon dioxide and various minerals, they make their own food. They needn't move. All that is needed comes to them. Sunlight bathes them (provided they remain in the uppermost layers of the ocean), while carbon dioxide and minerals are in the water all around. Life is not a struggle for them in the same way that it is for us.

The more complicated land plants must specialize considerably more than do the ocean plants. Land plants have stems, leaves, flowers, roots and so on, each made up of characteristic varieties of cell. Yet land plants, too, avoid much of the struggle of life. The carbon dioxide they need is absorbed from the air and their leaves spread out to catch the sunlight. Water is less available on "dry land" than in the ocean, of course, but land plants provide for themselves by developing a system of probing roots that fill the ground beneath their stems. These roots soak up water as blotting paper does and the water slowly reaches all parts of the plant through special cell systems, carrying with it dissolved minerals from the soil.

All this, whether on land or sea, is a simple, slow way of life, but the plant pays what seems to us an overwhelming price. It is self-sufficient, to be sure, and need not seek for food, but its way of life leaves it motionless and, for the most part, defenseless. Some plants develop thorns or poisons, but even such defenses are purely passive. In fact, a plant scarcely lives at all; it "vegetates."

But there is another group of living things, the animal kingdom, which has sacrificed the ability to manufacture food out of simple compounds, using the energy of sunlight. It is, instead, a kingdom of robbers which raid the food supplies so slowly and painstakingly built up by plants. What a plant may take months to gather up and develop an animal can recklessly tear down in days.

With concentrated food at its disposal, the animal can, and does, use up energy at a far greater rate than the plant. This has its disadvantages. The animal is more quickly affected by a bad run of luck than the plant. The animal can be more quickly killed by a temporary shortage of food, water or air.

A high rate of energy expenditure has its advantages, too. The animal has enough energy at hand to become free-moving, to develop muscles and build weapons of offense.

In order to do so more efficiently, animal cells that have joined together to form a complex organism must specialize far more than plant cells. Some become muscle cells capable of contracting and relaxing. Others become nerve cells that can sense changes in the environment and respond by stimulating other cells to do whatever is appropriate. There are cells that manufacture specific chemicals for use by the rest of the body, while still others are designed to protect the body's surface.

As animals increased in number and swarmed the oceans, they began competing among themselves. (In many cases, this competition took the form of one kind of animal learning to eat another, rifling the stored energy that had already been stolen from plants.) The animals that survived were those that made use of the environment most efficiently. Increased size and specialization was not the only road to efficiency (after all, there are innumerable one-celled creatures living and flourishing today), but certainly it was one of the roads. As millions of years passed, animals did increase in size and did specialize more and more.

Size brought problems. As cells massed together in increasing numbers, some began to pass out of reach of the ocean. They were buried away in the central regions of the animal with many layers of other cells between themselves and the ocean. How was food to reach these hidden cells? How was oxygen to reach them? What were they to do with the waste products they formed?

It was as though a table were loaded with food for a hundred but were only just large enough to seat five. The five people lucky enough to be seated at the table could eat their fill. Those standing just behind them would be able to get some food by reaching for it. But those further back and beyond arm's reach would starve to death, no matter how much food there was on the table, unless special provisions were made. There is a limit, and one that was quickly reached, to the size to which an animal might grow unless it made those special provisions.

Fortunately, there was a solution. The growing mass of cells did not form a solid mass but instead formed a shell, leaving a hollow at the center. Into this center a bit of ocean could enter; a bit of ocean that bathed the inner portion of the mass as the ocean itself bathed the outer.

The cells at or near the exterior surface of the animal body were bathed by the ocean directly, so they were no problem. The cells at or near the interior surface of the animal, the lining of the gut or intestine, that is, were bathed by the ocean water being continually swallowed by the animal, so they were no problem either. Finally, those crucial cells that were remote from both the exterior and interior surfaces of the creature were bathed by the trapped pinch of ocean within the very tissues of the animal, so their problem was solved, too.

Of course, it wasn't quite that simple. The animal had to devise ways of getting food and oxygen into this internal pinch of ocean so that the interior cells bathed by it could always have their supply. Furthermore, the interior cells discharged wastes into the pinch of ocean and the animal had to transfer these wastes into the great ocean outside. It meant more specialization; the development of new types of cells to help form gills and kidneys.

As animals continued to increase in size, a simple tube of internal ocean was insufficient. In order to reach all the cells, the tube of internal ocean had to branch again and again, reaching through all the tissues in an increasingly complicated network so that no cell might fail to have an "ocean front" or at least be very close to one.

Each solution, however, raises new problems. Suppose food and oxygen from outside have been transferred into an internal ocean filling one of these complicated networks of tubing. Can one rely on the food and oxygen percolating into all the crevices and crannies? Could they possibly percolate quickly enough to bring nourishment to an impatient cell far up one of the internal creeks and inlets?

The answer is no. Except for very small animals, one could not rely on ordinary percolation to do the job. The internal ocean must be converted into an internal river. The liquid must be circulated; necessities of life must be carried to the cell and not merely allowed to drift to it.

So the organism had to develop a pump which would keep the internal river constantly flowing.

When this happened, the cells were so efficiently taken care of that the way was open for animals to reach almost any size. The efficiency of the internal river became so great that many animals abandoned altogether the external ocean as their direct source of food supply and waste disposal. They converted the outer surface into a means of defense instead, thickening it, covering it with scales, shells or bony plates.

Furthermore, increasing size and power meant that some animals found it useful to develop some sort of internal stiffening device, first gristle and later bone, to keep the mass of cells reasonably rigid and to give muscles something firm to hold on to while they were contracting.

Finally, once animals grew independent of the direct use of the ocean, a group of them abandoned it as their habitat as well, and invaded first the fresh water of rivers and lakes and then the dry land itself. But even on land, animals carried their internal river of ocean water with them; still living in the ocean, however far away they went, but living in an ocean under their own control.

The adventurous land animals learned many more tricks. They had to develop lungs, instead of gills, to make use of the gaseous oxygen in the air, and then they had to evolve a more complicated pump in order to use that oxygen to better advantage.

During all this time, the river of sea-water within the animal was becoming more and more complicated. It was filled with special cells that detached themselves from the body and lived in the river. Special compounds were formed by the animals and dissolved in the river, which thus took on a thousand tasks that the original ocean had never been expected to fill.

In fact, the sea-water became much more than sea-water. It became a living river of blood. The tubes that carry it are the blood vessels. The pump that circulates it is the heart.

And without this living river of blood, any form of life more complex than a vegetating plant or a tiny, primitive animal composed of a handful of cells is impossible.

Mankind has never had any trouble understanding that blood was one of the things that made life possible. Even before the days of modern science and medicine, ages before in fact, it must have been noticed that continued bleeding led to progressive weakening and finally to death; not just in man, but in any animal. It was as though life poured out with the blood.

Even when death followed an infectious disease, or a blow which did not draw blood, or when it simply came on suddenly and mysteriously, there was one sure symptom of death —the heart no longer beat. The only other phenomenon that distinguished death from sleep or unconsciousness, or from a cataleptic trance, was that breathing stopped as well. But that was not as crucial. After all, breathing could be stopped at will for as long as several minutes, whereas the heart could not voluntarily be stopped for an instant.

If anything, pre-scientific man overestimated the role of heart and blood. He made the heart the seat of the emotions, perhaps because its rate of action is very noticeably affected by emotion; and ancient peoples often considered blood to be actually synonymous with life. Certainly, the ancient Hebrews had this idea and it is clearly stated in the Bible. In Genesis 1: 29-30, God addresses man after having created him on the sixth day of creation: "Behold, I have given you every herb bearing seed, which is upon the face of all the earth, and every tree, in the which is the fruit of a tree yielding seed; to you it shall be for meat. And to every beast of the earth, and to every fowl of the air, and to every thing that creepeth upon the earth, wherein there is life, I have given every green herb for meat . . ."

This passage seems to distinguish vegetation from the mineral world only in that vegetation bears seeds; it has the capacity for reproduction. But it is not described any further than "every herb bearing seed . . . every tree . . . yielding seed." It is to the animal kingdom only that the word "life" is applied: ". . . every beast . . . every fowl . . . every thing that creepeth . . . wherein there is life . . ."

From the Biblical point of view, life is the gift of God and no creature may be deprived of life except by God. Therefore, man and the animals were originally granted only the plant kingdom for food. The plants were bloodless, hence not really alive.

Even after the expulsion from Eden, vegetarianism remained the command; it was even made more rigorous. One of the punishments for the disobedience of Adam and Eve was the further restriction of their diet. God says (Genesis 3: 17-18): ". . . cursed is the ground for thy sake; in sorrow shalt thou eat of it all the days of thy life; thorns also and thistles shall it bring forth to thee; and thou shalt eat the herb of the field . . ."

Previously, "every herb . . . every tree . . . shall be for meat." Now, for the first time, the earth was to yield not voluntarily, but only after painful cultivation, and even then a variety of inedible plants, "thorns . . . and thistles," were also to come into existence. Yet in spite of the decrease in the general edibility of the plant kingdom, the command was clear: "thou shalt eat the herb of the field."

It was only after the Flood that an extension of man's diet was allowed. In Genesis 9: 2-3, God says to Noah: "And the fear of you and the dread of you shall be upon every beast of the earth, and upon every fowl of the air, upon all that moveth upon the earth, and upon all the fishes of the sea; into your hand are they delivered. Every moving thing that liveth shall be meat for you; even as the green herb have I given you all things."

Now, in other words, man might be carnivorous. Perhaps the liberalization of his diet was necessary in view of the destruction of food supplies by the Flood, and the necessity of rapid multiplication on the part of the survivors, but the Bible does not say this.

Instead, it goes on to stress the fact that the new covenant does not affect the sacredness of life. Life was still the gift of God and might not be taken away except by God. In the verse following those quoted above, in Genesis 9: 4, God says: "But flesh with the life thereof, which is the blood thereof, shall ye not eat."

The Hebrew concept then seemed to be that it was the blood of an animal that was the essence of life, ". . . the life . . . is the blood . . ." and that once the blood was removed, what was left of the animal was as unliving as any bloodless plant and might therefore be eaten with impunity.

This is even more clearly stated in the book of Leviticus, which contains detailed instructions to the Hebrew priests as to their manner of conducting sacrifices. In each case where an animal is involved, special attention is given to the manner of disposing of its blood. The first instruction always involves the blood. In Leviticus 1: 5, God says: "And he shall kill the bullock before the Lord: and the priests, Aaron's sons, shall bring the blood, and sprinkle the blood round about upon the altar . . ."

In other words, the life of the creature, in the form of the blood, is restored to God by way of the altar at the earliest moment after death. After that is done, then the rest of the animal, which is without life, may be washed, burnt, eaten according to instructions.

To this very day, Orthodox Jews, before preparing meat to be eaten, remove as much of the blood as possible.

Something of this mystical attitude toward blood persisted in much later times among Europeans who did not adhere to the Mosaic laws. It was widely believed, for instance, that contracts with the devil had to be signed in blood. What, after all, could be more binding than to sign with a piece of life itself when the soul was at stake? In Goethe's *Faust*, Mephistopheles says, *"Blut ist ein ganz besonderes Saft,"* meaning "Blood is quite a special fluid." And of course, so it is, though not necessarily for Mephistopheles' reasons.

Few of us in these days take such views seriously. We may enjoy rare steaks and sign important papers in ink, yet still the feeling about the special quality of blood persists in our common expressions.

A hearty, virile man is "red-blooded"; an aristocrat is "blue-blooded." A brave man is "stout-hearted"; a coward, "faint-hearted." Blood is commonly spoken of as though it determined the nature of a man and we speak of "noble blood" and "bad blood." People descended from a common ancestor are spoken of as having the "same blood" and we speak of "blood relatives" as opposed to "relatives by marriage."

This attitude doesn't confine itself to metaphors only. There are still people who think that blood is more intimately connected with life than other parts of the body and that human characteristics can be transferred from one man to another along with a transfer of blood. During World War II, for instance, there were efforts made to keep the Red Cross from pooling the blood of American Negroes with the blood of their fellow Americans of paler skin, for purely superstitious reasons since there is no greater difference between the blood of Negroes and whites than there is among samples of blood taken from different white individuals.

Yet though the heart is not the seat of the emotions; though the blood is neither identical with life nor the part of a man that determines his character and personality, the actual properties of blood are far more amazing and even awe-inspiring than man's mythological fancies about it.

Chapter 2

The Watery Background

WATER IS the general background of life. The chemical reactions that go on in living tissues involve molecules that are floating in water or that are located along a surface membrane bathed by water. The reactions very frequently involve the water molecules themselves.

This should not be surprising. Life began in the oceans and it has never left it. Inside, we're still ocean.

The only tissues in our body that are low in water content are adipose tissue (fat) and skeleton (bone). These are only about 25 per cent water. Both adipose tissue and skeleton, however, are rather inactive. This is not to say that they are not alive or that nothing goes on in them. It is just that less goes on in them than in other tissues of the body. In the furious traffic of life chemistry, fat and bone are comparatively quiet side-streets.

Blood seems to be at the other extreme. As it is liquid you might suppose it contains more water than do the other tissues. Actually, this is not particularly true.

If we forget adipose tissue and the skeleton, the rest of the tissues of the body are from 70 to 85 per cent water. Blood is just a bit above average in this respect. It is 80 per cent water. The heart itself is 80 per cent water, so are the kidneys; and these are "solid" tissues. In fact, the most watery of all the tissues of the body is a solid tissue, the gray matter of the brain. This is 85 per cent water.

Yet gray matter is solid and blood is liquid. For all its water content, the gray matter of the brain is made up of cells that are joined together and held in place. Blood also contains cells but these are not joined together and are not held in place. The cells in blood float singly and separately in liquid. Blood moves and the cells are carried along by the current.

If the only function of blood were to move the blood cells from place to place, any liquid would do. If life had happened to develop in an ocean of some liquid other than water (assuming this to be possible), that other liquid would be doing that particular job about as well as water would.

However, blood has many other functions to perform, and for a number of reasons, no liquid that exists could possibly do as well as water.

For instance, of all common substances water is the best solvent; that is, it will dissolve the largest variety of substances without seriously damaging their molecules in the process. Out of personal experience, we all know, for instance, that table salt, sodium bicarbonate, sugar and alcohol are among the common substances that will dissolve easily in water. There are thousands of others that will dissolve just as easily; and thousands more that will dissolve only slightly but still enough to matter.

The result is that the watery liquid of the blood carries with it, in its circulation, not only cells but also all sorts of substances in solution. No other liquid would carry so many so well; therefore no other liquid would make possible as many different reactions; no other liquid would allow living tissues so much chemical versatility.

There is a second way in which water excels as the liquid of the living river. But this requires a more complicated explanation and I've got to approach it by way of a little more evolutionary history.

When animal life first ventured out of the water and onto dry land, it found an environment which was, by and large, much harsher than the ocean surroundings to which, for millions of years, it had been accustomed.

For one thing, the open air varied in temperature from day to day and from season to season. On a particular day there might be a 20 or 30 degree spread between the temperature of the afternoon and that of the dawn. There could be a 100 degree spread, or more, between summer and winter. In the ocean, on the other hand, except for a thin layer at the surface of the tropic oceans, the temperature was constant day and night, winter and summer. (That constant temperature, by the way, is near the freezing point, but that is no hardship. Gases dissolve to a greater extent in cold water than in warm water, so that cold water contains more oxygen than warm water does and actually supports a heavier load of life.)

The early forms of land life, including invertebrates such as snails and insects, and vertebrates such as amphibians and reptiles, surrendered to the temperature changes of the new medium. They remained "cold-blooded."

This does not mean that the blood of such animals was refrigerated. It merely means that their bodies take on approximately the temperature of the air about them. Since only a few days a year have temperatures that are higher than the nearly 100 degree F. of our own bodies (and then at most only for a few hours at a time), the temperature of a "cold-blooded" animal is almost always lower than ours. The animal is "cold-blooded" by comparison with ourselves.

Cold-bloodedness has its disadvantages. If the temperature of the environment drops below the freezing point of water, so does that of the cold-blooded animal. If the water within the animal freezes, the animal will die. The only way a cold-blooded animal can survive a freezing winter is to die and let eggs survive till spring, or return itself temporarily to the water (underneath any surface layer of ice that may have formed) or migrate to a warmer climate or go into hibernation in some spot which is protected from the worst of the cold. The ocean, except for a surface layer in the Polar regions, never freezes, so this problem never arises among sea-creatures.

Furthermore, chemical reactions go faster as the temperature goes up; slower as it goes down. That is why you can tell the temperature by counting the rate at which a cricket chirps. The chirping is caused by the motion of legs against wings. This depends on the rate at which the leg muscles contract, which depends on the rate at which certain chemical reactions take place within the muscle cells, which depends on the temperature of those muscle cells, which (finally) depends on the tempearture of the air about the cricket.

The chemistry of a cold-blooded animal is geared to run

at a comfortable speed at some average warm-season temperature. When the temperature drops, the cold-blooded animal becomes sluggish.

Any creature that could devise a means by which, whatever the outside temperature, it could itself remain comfortably warm, would have a tremendous advantage over its cold-blooded fellows. It could live comfortably in areas of the world and at times of the year that are too cold for cold-blooded animals. On any cool day, it could run faster, react more quickly than a cold-blooded animal. It could easily escape the clutches of a large cold-blooded animal and easily catch and eat a small cold-blooded animal.

There is no doubt that "warm-bloodedness" was the key to a more successful life and the most highly developed animals of today, the birds and the mammals, are warm-blooded.

The source of the heat is no problem. The chemical reactions in the body supply copious heat. The only problem is to keep the heat from being lost through the skin to the outside air too quickly.

One way for an animal to conserve its heat is to be large. The larger an animal is, the less surface it has in proportion to its body weight. If the weight of a mouse were suddenly increased a hundred times without its shape being changed, its body would produce a hundred times as much heat altogether. However, the area exposed by the mouse to the outside world, its skin area, would be increased only tenfold. It would lose heat only ten times as fast.

All things considered, then, large animals conserve their body heat more efficiently than small ones. That may have been one of the reasons why some of the cold-blooded dinosaurs and related reptiles grew to such huge size. It may also be one of the reasons for the large size of some of our modern warm-blooded animals of the Arctic regions: the whales, walruses and polar bears.

There is another way of cutting down heat loss besides increasing body weight. Air itself is a very poor conductor of heat. If a layer of air would only hold still around an animal body, the heat of that body would be lost quite slowly even on cold days. The trouble is that a layer of air won't hold still. Even if a wind of some sort weren't blowing, the animal's own motion would stir up the air about it. And it is the moving air that deprives an animal of its heat.

How can an animal contrive to keep a still layer of air about itself? Two different groups of animals solved that problem in two different ways. The ancestors of the mammals developed hair; the ancestors of the birds developed feathers. (Both were developed out of the original reptilian scales.) Hair and feathers act to trap a layer of "dead air" next to the skin and cut down heat loss; feathers, by the way, are the more efficient of the two. With heat loss cut down, the natural heat of the chemical reactions within a body will keep birds and mammals warm even on cold days.

Man, who has lost most of his body covering of hair, has replaced it with artificial coverings in the form of clothing during the day and blankets at night. These keep that layer of dead air next to the skin. Whales, which have also lost their hair, and returned, moreover, to the near-freezing cold of the ocean, have developed a layer of fat, the so-called "blubber," inches thick just under the skin. Fat, too, is a good insulator against heat loss.

With heat loss cut down, the reverse problem arises. On warm days, too much heat may accumulate. Alternatively, in periods of unusual activity, chemical reactions will speed up, producing abnormally high quantities of heat, so that again too much may accumulate. It follows that warm-blooded animals, having learned to conserve heat, must also learn how to get rid of it when occasion warrants.

You and I, for instance, possess sweat glands that continually discharge water onto the surface of our skins. There it evaporates, the liquid water being converted into gaseous water vapor. Now water vapor contains more energy than liquid water of the same temperature. Therefore, in order for the liquid perspiration to turn to vapor, heat, the most common form of energy, must be supplied. The necessary heat is taken from the most available place; that is, from the skin with which the perspiration is in contact.

In other words, the evaporation of sweat cools the skin. On cool days, you sweat less, so that the cooling is less. On warm days or on occasions of unusual activity, you sweat more and the cooling is more.

Perspiration is, in this way, a kind of natural air-conditioning system. It is the ability to perspire that enables a human being to survive for a while at temperatures hot enough to boil water. If the scorching air is kept perfectly dry, perspiration will be formed and will evaporate quickly enough to remove heat from the body faster than the hot air will transfer it to the body.

The value of the air-conditioning system is made quite plain to us on occasions when it is overloaded. We may be so active that the heat produced is more than the perspiration can handle. Perspiration is produced faster than it can evaporate and visible drops of it collect on the skin. Or else the day may be hot and humid so that evaporation is slowed down to the point where visible drops will collect even if we remain perfectly still. In either case, the failure of our air-conditioning makes us quite uncomfortable.

Another method of regulating the temperature of the body involves the blood. A part of the body which is particularly active chemically will tend to have a temperature higher than the rest of the body. A part which is near the usually cold surrounding air will tend to have a temperature lower than that of the rest.

It is the blood that equalizes these differences of temperature as it circulates. It absorbs heat when passing through active organs such as the liver. It releases heat when passing through cooler tissues such as the skin. In doing so, it cools the liver and warms the skin.

On hot days, the body loses heat slowly to the warm air that surrounds it. The body compensates for that by dilating the small blood vessels in the skin, "vasodilatation." It does this by relaxing the tiny muscles in the walls of the blood vessels. Once dilated, the blood vessels will hold more blood so that more of the blood's heat will be exposed to the air. This tends to make up for the fact that heat is being lost more slowly. This is why your face is flushed on a hot day, or after strenuous work or exercise, when a greater than normal amount of heat has been produced in your muscles.

On the other hand, when the surrounding temperature is colder than usual, the rate of heat loss from the body is increased and the body must compensate for that. One way is to tighten the muscles of the small vessels and constrict them, "vasoconstriction." In this way, blood is forced out of the skin and less heat is available for loss to the outside air. This is why you turn "blue with cold." Cold will also make you shiver so that you may produce more heat through muscular activity; and it will give you "goose-pimples" as the body tries to raise your ineffectual little hairs in an effort to trap a thicker layer of dead air.

What is the part played by water in the heat control effected by perspiration and by blood? To answer that, let's consider how much heat various substances can hold.

Suppose you had a pint of water at a temperature of 100° C., or 212° F. if you prefer the Fahrenheit scale; in either case, the water is at the boiling point. Suppose also, that you had a pint of ethyl alcohol at a temperature of 0° C. (or 32° F.), which is the temperature at which water freezes.

Now mix the two, the pint of hot water and the pint of cold alcohol, and assume that you have taken precautions to avoid losing significant quantities of either by evaporation while all this is taking place. You end up with a quart of alcohol-water mixture at some intermediate temperature. Common sense will tell you that the temperature of the mixture should be midway between the two given temperatures; that it would be 50° C. (122° F.).

Common sense is, however, wrong in this case (as it so often is). The final temperature will be more like 65° C. (150° F.).

Water, you see, will hold more heat than alcohol will. It takes more heat to raise the temperature of water than of alcohol. And as its temperature falls, it gives off more heat than does alcohol. The amount of heat given off by water in cooling 35 degrees is enough to heat up alcohol some 65 degrees.

It takes about 16½ calories of heat to raise the temperature of a cubic inch of water 1 degree Celsius. (The exact number of calories varies a bit according to the temperature you start with, but let's not worry about that.) At body temperature, it would take only about 10 calories of heat to raise the temperature of a cubic inch of ethyl alcohol 1 degree Celsius; and a mere 7¾ calories will do the trick for a cubic inch of olive oil.

Some familiar solids will hold even less heat than will olive oil. A cubic inch of glass at ordinary temperatures will rise 1 degree Celsius in temperature after absorbing somewhere between 2 and 3 calories of heat. (The exact figure depends on the variety of glass being considered.) Some metals do more poorly still. A cubic inch of copper at ordinary temperatures will go up 1 degree Celsius after absorbing 1½ calories. The figure for silver is about $9/_{10}$ calorie and that for gold only ½ calorie. The temperature of an empty tea-kettle on the fire will shoot up very quickly but a little water in the kettle on the same fire will warm up slowly

The amount of heat a substance will hold is called the *specific heat* and what I have really been trying to say is that the specific heat of water is higher than that of almost any other substance.

As the blood absorbs heat from the chemical reactions proceeding in the liver or in the working muscles, its temperature goes up less than it would if it were made up of any liquid other than water. As it loses heat passing near the skin, the temperature goes down less. The unusually high specific heat of water helps the blood equalize the temperature more efficiently.

Water has a similar effect on weather, by the way. The water of the ocean has a higher specific heat than the soil of dry land. Therefore the temperature of the ocean rises less than the temperature of the dry land under the influence of summer heat and falls less with the winter cold. That is why the ocean is a moderating and equalizing influence on temperature; why coastal areas are cooler in the summer than inland areas and warmer in the winter. The blood, as I have said, is our own private ocean and so our entire body, being bathed in it, is a coastal area.

Again, just as it takes unusual quantities of heat to raise the temperature of water, so it takes unusual quantities of heat to vaporize a given quantity of liquid water. It takes about 9,000 calories of heat to evaporate a cubic inch of water and only about one-third that amount to evaporate a cubic inch of alcohol. Chemists express this by saying that water has a higher *latent heat of vaporization* than almost any other substance.

To be sure, a drop of alcohol on the skin evaporates more quickly than water does and makes the skin feel cooler than water would. However, the alcohol is soon gone. A drop of water of equal size would last longer and, while working more slowly, would in the long run remove three times as much heat. Perspiration would simply not be as efficient an air-conditioner if it were composed of any common liquid other than water.

It is this high specific heat and latent heat of vaporization of water that I was thinking of when, early in the chapter, I referred to a second way in which water was particularly suitable to the workings of life.

Chapter 3

As We Live and Breathe

OF THE VARIOUS SUBSTANCES upon which we must depend in the world around us, air (or at least the oxygen in air) is the most crucial. We can go without drinking water for days, if we have to, and without food for weeks. I'm not saying the process of doing without either is pleasant, but our body can store both food and water to tide us over reasonable periods of shortage.

The situation is quite different as far as air is concerned. Block the windpipe for five minutes and you'll be dead.

Oxygen being such a critical commodity, the body needs a good working system for getting it to the consumer. And keep one thing firmly in mind; the consumer is not just you, or just your body. It is each of the trillions upon trillions of microscopic cells in your body. Each individual cell must have its own ample supply or that individual cell will die. It won't help any cell for its neighbor to have oxygen. It needs its own.

To begin with, obviously, we get oxygen by breathing. That, however, is only the first step. Just inhaling, all by itself, accomplishes nothing but to take a supply of air just outside our nose and move it into an air space within our chest. That alone doesn't help a cell in our big toe the least bit.

However, the oxygen once inside the lungs, continues on its travels. The inner lining of the lungs is covered with a thin film of water in which the oxygen dissolves. Air is one-fifth oxygen and four-fifths nitrogen. Nitrogen, which is useless to the body in the form in which it occurs in air, also dissolves in the film but for the present, I'll consider only the vitally needed oxygen.

Only the oxygen near the film of moisture has a chance to dissolve in it before you exhale again, push most of the air out of the lungs and bring in a new supply. If the lungs were just a pair of hollow bags, like football bladders, hardly any of the oxygen would be near enough to the inner surface to dissolve in the moisture film. Fortunately the lungs are much more than football bladders.

Air travels through the nose or mouth and enters the windpipe (the *trachea,* to use a fancier word). You can feel the windpipe in your neck above and below your Adam's apple. Just below your neck (where you can no longer feel it) the windpipe divides into two *bronchi* (singular, *bronchus*) and one enters each lung. Within the lung, the bronchi divide and subdivide over and over, like the very complicated branches of a tree. Each final tiny branchlet ends in a little hollow called an air sac or an *alveolus* (plural, *alveoli*). The lungs are filed with these tiny sacs, so that they resemble sponges.

When you breathe in, air is sucked into the millions and millions of these alveoli. Each little sac is equipped with a thin film of moisture along its inner surface, and the individual sac is so small that all the oxygen in it is fairly close to the moisture film. Counting all the alveoli together, there is an enormous amount of inner surface and, of course, moisture film that goes along with it. If the surface exposed by all the alveoli were smoothed out into a flat patch, it would cover about a thousand square feet, or the floor area of five good-sized livingrooms.

With all that moist surface into which the oxygen can dissolve, the result is that in the time between breathing in and breathing out, one-fifth of the oxygen in the air in your lungs enters the water film. The air you inhale is 20 per cent oxygen; the air you exhale is only 16 per cent oxygen. An ordinary quiet breath shoves about 30 cubic inches of air into and out of your lungs. Of that, 6 cubic inches is oxygen. Six cubic inches goes in, that is; but only a trifle under 5 cubic inches comes out and 1¼ cubic inches of oxygen is absorbed. (Of course, when the body is in the grip of muscular activity or of strong emotion, so that more oxygen is needed, breathing automatically becomes both deeper and more rapid.)

What happens to the oxygen after it dissolves in the moist inner film of the alveoli? The membrane that encloses the alveolus is extremely thin. It is only about one micron in thickness. (A *micron* is one of the units of the metric system of measurement, used by scientists the world over and by the ordinary peoples of all countries except the English-speaking ones. A micron is one millionth of a meter; a meter being equal to 1.1 yards. In ordinary American units, a micron is equal to one twenty-five thousandth [1/25,000th] of an inch. In dealing with tiny fractions of an inch it is obviously convenient to use microns as a unit of measurement.)

The alveolar membrane is too thin to be waterproof. Small molecules such as those of water (made up of three atoms each) or oxygen (made up of two atoms each) can leak right through, either by passing through tiny holes in the membrane, or by moving between the molecules that make up the membrane, or perhaps by some other method of which we're not yet aware.

A membrane that lets molecules through like that is said to be *permeable*. The process by which molecules drift through the body of a substance (whether gas, liquid or solid), or across a thin membrane, is called *diffusion*.

The membranes surrounding the alveoli only let small molecules through. There are many large molecules in the body, made up of hundreds or even thousands of atoms each. These could not pass the alveolar membrane. That membrane is therefore called a *semi-permeable membrane*. It is permeable to some molecules, in other words, but not to others.

All living cells are surrounded by semi-permeable membranes and this is a vitally important fact. If the cell were not able to keep some molecules permanently on the outside and others permanently on the inside, it would be no different in chemical composition from the outside environment; and no more alive either.

To pass on. Oxygen not only can pass through the alveolar membrane, but it tends to pass through mainly in one direction; that is, from the open space inside the alveolus through the membrane and into the body. There is considerable oxygen on the "air side" of the membrane and less oxygen on the "body side," and the oxygen molecule diffuses in the direction that would tend to equalize the quantity on both sides, (like water seeking its own level, whether it runs downhill as a brook or bubbles up from the ground as a spring).

Immediately on the other side of the alveolar membrane is a second membrane. This second membrane, no thicker than the first, makes up the wall of a tiny blood vessel called a *capillary*. (There is a capillary network hugging the "body side" of every alveolus.) The capillary wall is also a semi-permeable membrane. The oxygen molecules drift across this second membrane also, still seeking to equalize the oxygen content on both sides. Once an oxygen molecule has diffused through the capillary wall, it finds itself in the blood stream and another stage in its travels is done.

If you are wondering whether the blood stream simply carries the oxygen molecules to all parts of the body without further ado, and whether they then drift out of the capillary walls and into the cells all over the body the answer is a strenuous "No!" Carrying oxygen in the quantities needed by the body is not as simple as that and elaborate chemical machinery has been developed for the purpose.

Before going on to discuss the difficulties and solutions of oxygen-carrying, I should like to introduce you to a few more metric units.

A *liter* is the metric unit of volume. It is just a little bigger than an American quart, and somewhat smaller than a British quart. A *milliliter* is a thousandth of a liter. This is a fairly small unit; a cubic inch contains about 16.4 milliliters.

A *gram* is the metric unit of weight. It is a small unit. An ounce contains about 28.35 grams. A *milligram*, being but a thousandth of a gram, is smaller still.

Now, if pure oxygen is bubbled through a liter of ice water, some of the oxygen will dissolve in the water; not much, however. The liter of ice water will dissolve only 70 milligrams of oxygen.

That, mind you, is when pure oxygen is bubbled through the water. If the bubbles were ordinary air, which is only one-fifth oxygen, then only one-fifth the quantity of oxygen would dissolve. A liter of ice water would dissolve only 14 milligrams of oxygen. (Some nitrogen is also dissolved out of the air, but never mind that just now.)

It may seem to you that 14 milligrams (about 1/2000th of an ounce) per liter of water is so insignificant a quantity that we might as well ignore it; yet much of life depends upon that very small quantity. Fish and other animals that breathe through gills get their oxygen not from the immense quantities present in the atmosphere (they suffocate if taken out into the open air), but from the small quantity dissolved in water.

(Of course, we mustn't underestimate the oxygen dissolved in the ocean, either. The amount in one liter is small, but there are many liters of water in the ocean. A cubic mile of ocean water at freezing temperature would contain a total of 60,000 tons of dissolved oxygen and there are hundreds of cubic miles of ocean on Earth.)

You will notice that I keep talking about ice water. That is because the amount of gas which water can dissolve depends upon its temperature. The warmer the water gets, the less gas it can dissolve. A liter of water at 37° C. (the temperature of the human body) will dissolve only about half the oxygen that ice water will; only 7 milligrams.

But let's leave the ocean and get back to blood. How much oxygen will our blood dissolve? To answer that, we must ask another question first. How much blood is there in the human body?

This, actually, is not a very easy thing to determine. The most direct way of doing so would be to take a newly-dead body, drain all the blood out of it and measure the volume. One of the troubles is that it is just about impossible to get all the blood out of a body. An indefinite quantity always remains behind in the microscopic capillaries.

A more indirect, but much better, method is to take a known amount of a harmless dye solution and inject it into a vein. The dye is carried through the circulatory system, mixing with the blood as it goes. After allowing enough time for thorough mixing, a sample of blood is withdrawn. You can tell from the color of the blood how much the original dye has been thinned out. (The color of the dyed blood must be compared with the color of the original blood and of the original dye. This is not done by naked eye but by sensitive instruments, photoelectric colorimeters, that make use of photocells plus either special filters or quartz prisms to allow only the light of certain colors to hit the photocells.) If the color of the dye in the blood after mixing is only one thousandth as intense as it was to start with, it has mixed with one thousand times its own original volume. Since we know the original volume of the dye, we can easily calculate the volume of the blood.

But there are errors involved here, too. Some of the dye always leaks out of the blood stream, for instance. Still, by use of this method and others like it, we arrive at the fact that from 6 to 8 per cent of the body weight is blood. It varies slightly from person to person and is higher in men than in women. To put it another way, for every kilogram of body weight (a *kilogram* is equal to 1,000 grams or to 2.2 pounds), there are about 77 milliliters of blood in men and 66 milliliters in women. A 70-kilogram man (154 pounds) would contain about 5.4 liters of blood. A 50-kilogram woman (110 pounds) would contain about 3.3 liters of blood.

But of the total quantity of blood, only some 80 per cent is water and it is mainly in the water portion that the oxygen dissolves. The quantity of water in the blood vessels of our 70-kilogram "average man" is about 4.3 liters. This quantity of water, at body heat, would dissolve 4.3×7 milligrams of oxygen or just about 30 milligrams.

Now the amount of oxygen the average male adult needs, assuming he lies still in a warm room and does nothing at all, is not less than about 23,400 milligrams per hour or about 390 milligrams per minute.

This seems to work out fairly well. With each breath, our body absorbs about 20 milliliters of oxygen (this is about 1¼ cubic inches). Since ordinary quiet breathing is at the rate of 16 breaths per minute, it means that we absorb about 450 milligrams of oxygen per minute. (1 milliliter of oxygen weighs 1.43 milligrams.) This is enough to keep us going at something better than the minimum. It allows us to do more than just lie down quietly.

Of course, if a man starts working, his oxygen requirement goes up, but he also starts breathing more quickly. On the other hand, a woman, with less water in her blood vessels absorbs less oxygen, but she also needs less than a man does because, in the first place, the average woman has a smaller weight of body to keep going, and secondly, a larger percentage of the female body is fat, which requires less than average upkeep in the way of energy derived from oxygen.

But compare the amount of oxygen dissolved in the blood of the average man, 30 milligrams, and his minimum requirement for oxygen, 390 milligrams per minute. Even assuming that the blood can make the transfer from lungs to cells quickly enough, there is still only a 4½ second supply of oxygen in the blood at any one time. If that were the true situation, it would mean that any stoppage of the breath would be followed by death in seconds.

But this is just not so. You can probably hold your breath for a minute, or even two, if you force yourself, without even losing consciousness. And people have been under water, or stopped breathing for other reasons, for considerably longer than that and have still been brought back to consciousness by artificial respiration. So there must be more oxygen in the body than can be accounted for by the amount that can be dissolved in the blood

In fact, if you take a quantity of blood and place it under a vacuum so that all the gases it contains come bubbling out, you can measure how much of the gas is oxygen. It turns out that a liter of blood that has just passed through the lungs and picked up its oxygen supply is carrying no less than 285 milligrams of oxygen or about fifty times as much as the water in that quantity of blood can be expected to dissolve.

The next question, then, is this: where does all that oxygen come from? Two per cent of that oxygen was held in solution. The other 98 per cent must have been held by the blood in some other way.

If a drop of blood is placed under the microscope, you will see, that it contains small bodies distributed through the liquid background. These bodies are called *formed elements*, because they have a definite shape and form as compared with the featureless liquid background.

If a sample of blood is placed in a test-tube and the test-tube is then spun round rapidly (the instrument that does the spinning is called a *centrifuge*), the formed elements in the blood are pressed down against the bottom of the test-tube by centrifugal force. If the test-tube is then removed, the lower half of its contents is a dark red mass of formed elements squeezed tightly together. The upper half has been freed of the formed elements and what is left is a straw-colored liquid called *blood plasma,* or, often, simply *plasma.*

More precisely, the formed elements make up about 45 per cent of the volume of the blood and the liquid plasma makes up the remaining 55 per cent. (You may feel confused at this point, because earlier I said blood was 80 per cent water, but don't forget that the formed elements contain considerable water in their own makeup. For that matter, blood plasma is by no means entirely water. It works out this way: formed elements are about 65 to 70 per cent water; plasma is about 92 per cent water; blood as a whole or, as it is often called, *whole blood,* is, as stated earlier, 80 per cent water.)

There are three kinds of formed bodies present in blood. In order of decreasing size, these are:

1   The *leucocytes,* or *white cells*
2   The *erythrocytes,* or *red cells*
3   The *thrombocytes,* or *platelets*

I will have occasion to talk about each of these, but it is the red cell that carries the oxygen-handling machinery, so I will talk about it now and save the others for later occasions.

The red cells (and "erythrocyte" just means "red cell" in Greek) are not complete cells. A complete cell contains a central region marked off from the rest of the cell by a thin membrane and called the *cell nucleus.* The part of the cell outside the nucleus is called the *cytoplasm.* The cytoplasm carries on much of the ordinary chemical business of the cell but it is the nucleus that is in charge of the mechanisms that lead to the reproduction of the cell; that is, to its division into two new cells.

The human red cell contains no nucleus. It is originally formed in the bone marrow of the skull, ribs and vertebrae. In children, it is also formed in the marrow at the ends of the long bones of the arms and legs. It starts out as a large cell with a nucleus and without its characteristic red coloring matter. It is then called a *megaloblast.* This gains the coloring matter to become an *erythroblast.* Then, as it continues to multiply, it shrinks in size to become a *normocyte.* It then loses its nucleus and becomes a *reticulocyte.* The reticulocytes are released into the blood stream and within a few hours are full-fledged red cells. In normal blood, one red cell in every two hundred is still in the reticulocyte stage.

The red cell goes about its duties in the blood and does its work but, without a nucleus, it can grow and divide no more. When it is worn out, it breaks up. It leaves no descendants. New freshly-made red cells must replace it. Because of its lack of a nucleus, the name "cell" is sometimes denied it; it is often called a *red corpuscle* instead.

The red cell is smaller than ordinary cells, too. The white cell, for instance, (which is a normal cell, complete with nucleus) has a diameter of 10 to 20 microns. The red cell, on the other hand, is only 7½ microns in diameter. This is not much larger than the nuclei of ordinary cells; smaller than some nuclei, in fact. The red cell is shaped like a disc, or coin, and is about 2 microns thick. The disc is biconcave; that is, the centers of the flat sides are pressed in, like a candy "Life-saver" with the hole not bored through completely. (Sometimes the red cells are called *red discs*.)

The individual red cell is not red in color but is more or less straw-colored. However, when red cells pile up in quantity the color appears a deep red. And they do pile up in quantity, for their shape is such that in blood, they tend to come together in stacks, like poker-chips.

Red cells can be counted by diluting a known quantity of blood with salt solution of a certain strength and placing a drop of the diluted blood on a microscope slide, which has been divided up into very tiny squares. By counting the red cells on each of a number of the squares, one can calculate how many there must have been in the blood to begin with.

It turns out that in the blood of an adult male there are 5,400,000 red cells in every cubic millimeter; the figure for the adult female is 4,800,000.

A cubic millimeter is a very small unit of volume. There are 16,387 cubic millimeters in one cubic inch, and there are 280 cubic inches of blood in the average 150-pound man. Our average man therefore possesses, altogether, 25,000,000,000,000 (twenty-five trillion) red cells. If he were to parcel out his red cells, one man would have enough to supply every man, woman and child on earth with over 8,000 of them.

The body contains a blood reservoir in the form of the *spleen*, a fist-sized organ behind and above the stomach. It contains spaces ("sinuses") filled with blood that is particularly rich in red cells. An additional 5,000,000,000,000 (five trillion) are thus held in reserve. Contraction of the spleen during muscular exercise or on hot days or during sudden fright pushes some of these into the blood.

A woman weighs less than a man, and she has less blood than a man, even for her weight, and fewer red cells in each drop of blood. An average 120-pound woman would have a total of 17,000,000,000,000 (seventeen trillion) red cells. This is only two-thirds of a man's supply but women seem to get along just as well. (In fact, they get along better. The average woman in the United States lives some three years longer than the average man and she is considerably less susceptible to disorders of the circulatory system.)

The red cell is made up largely of *hemoglobin* and water, contained inside a semi-permeable membrane.

Hemoglobin is a *protein* (the name given to certain very important and complex molecules in the body). The hemoglobin molecule is quite large, being made up of thousands of individual atoms of six different varieties. Its size (or the size of any molecule) is measured by a quantity called the *molecular weight*. This compares the weight of the molecule to the weight of an oxygen atom which is arbitrarily set at 16·000. Thus, a hydrogen molecule (made up of two hydrogen atoms, which are the smallest atoms of all) has a molecular weight of only 2. A water molecule (made up of two hydrogen atoms plus an oxygen atom) has a molecular weight of 18. A molecule of hemoglobin, however, has a molecular weight of fully 68,000.

As far as oxygen-carrying is concerned the most important part of the hemoglobin molcule are the four iron atoms each contains. A molecule of hemoglobin, if it finds itself in the neighborhood of oxygen molecules, can attach those molecules loosely to itself to form a new substance called *oxyhemoglobin*. The point of attachment is at the iron atom, which is what makes the iron atoms so important. Since there are four iron atoms per molecule of hemoglobin, each molecule of hemoglobin is capable of carrying up to four molecules of oxygen.

Now let's go back again to the little capillaries that hug each alveolus of the lung. The capillaries are so fine that even a single red cell, small though it is, has trouble getting through. It has to squeeze a little to make it (like a man working his way through a narrow tunnel on hands and knees) and is forced to travel slowly.

The oxygen molecules that have diffused across the alveolar membrane and then across the capillary wall now have time enough to diffuse across the semi-permeable membrane of the red cell as the latter nudges its slow way along the capillary. Once inside the red cell, the oxygen molecule clicks into place alongside one of the iron atoms of one of the hemoglobin molecules. The red cell is so small that oxygen molecules can find their way into any part of it before the red cell has had time to leave the neighborhood of the alveoli. A red cell leaving the lung has oxygen molecules hanging on to about 95 per cent of the iron atoms in the hemoglobin it contains.

This is a much more efficient way of carrying oxygen than by depending on the oxygen to dissolve in the water of the blood. A single red cell contains about 270,000,000 (two hundred seventy million) hemoglobin molecules. With each hemoglobin molecule carrying four oxygen molecules, one red cell would contain just over 1,000,000,000 (one billion) molecules of oxygen. If a red cell consisted of water only, the number of molecules of oxygen it could carry, just by dissolving them in the water, would be only 14,000,000 (fourteen million). The red cell is thus many times as efficient an oxygen-carrier as water alone would be and that explains why we can hold our breath as long as we do.

Still, we must remember that the hemoglobin of the blood represents the total oxygen reservoir of the body. Even with every hemoglobin molecule carrying oxygen there would still only be a few minutes supply. So day and night, year in, year out, we must keep breathing.

In order to continue the story of oxygen, I must stop and say a few words about the heart and blood vessels.

The heart is a hollow muscle. The hollow is divided vertically into two halves, one on the right and one on the left. Each half is divided again horizontally, so that altogether the heart is divided into four compartments. The upper compartments are called *auricles* and the lower compartments are *ventricles*. The heart is thus made up of a left auricle, a left ventricle, a right auricle and a right ventricle.

Let's start with the right ventricle. As the heart contracts, it squeezes the blood out of the right ventricle. The blood cannot move up into the auricle above, since the auricles are fitted with one-way valves. Blood can pass from auricle to ventricle easily, but not vice versa unless the heart is diseased. The blood squeezed out of the right ventricle moves out of the heart altogether, therefore, and into a blood-vessel known as the *pulmonary artery*. "Artery" is the name given to any large vessel that carries blood moving away from the heart.

The pulmonary artery leads the blood toward the lungs. It divides and subdivides until it ends at the lungs as the fine network of capillaries I have already mentioned. In these capillaries, the hemoglobin molecules of the red cells pick up oxygen and become oxyhemoglobin.

The blood passes slowly out of the capillaries and begins to head away from the lung and back toward the heart. The capillaries meet once again to form larger and still larger vessels till, finally, they have all joined in the *pulmonary vein*. "Vein" is the name given to any large vessel that carries blood toward the heart, and "pulmonary," by the way, comes from the Latin word for "lung."

Through the pulmonary vein the blood rushes toward the heart with its full load of oxyhemoglobin and finds itself tumbling into the left auricle. From the left auricle, the blood passes, by way of a one-way valve, into the left ventricle. As the heart contracts again, the blood spurts, at a speed of a mile an hour (or 80 feet a minute) into the largest artery in the body, the *aorta*. Several arteries, including the *carotid artery*, branch off the aorta near its beginning and lead to the head and arms. The main portion of the aorta continues down the trunk and about the small of the back divides into the two *iliac arteries*, which lead to the pelvis and down the legs. All the large branches divide and subdivide into small vessels called *arterioles*, and then into a fine network of capillaries permeating all the body except for the lungs.

The red cells find themselves, once again, nudging along very narrow capillaries and moving at a speed of only an inch a minute. This time, on the other side of the capillary wall, there is no crowd of waiting oxygen molecules. Instead, there is a crowd of cells, each hungry for oxygen. The oxyhemoglobin has only a loose hold on the oxygen molecules and these oxygen molecules, obeying the blind force which makes them tend to equalize in quantity on both sides of a membrane, let go of the oxyhemoglobin molecule, drift across the red cell membrane, across the capillary wall, across the semi-permeable membranes that surround each cell, and, finally, into the cell.

Gradually, in this way, the oxyhemoglobin in the red cells is converted back to hemoglobin. Gradually, the blood loses its supply of oxygen. By the time the blood has worked its way through the capillaries, the oxygen is just about all gone. The capillaries once more start combining into *venules*, then into larger and larger veins until the "used up" blood finds itself in the *inferior vena cava* (carrying the blood back to the heart from the legs and torso) and the *superior vena cava* (carrying the blood back to the heart from the head and arms). These join and enter the right auricle.

The blood, once in the right auricle, passes on into the right ventricle and then is squeezed out into the pulmonary artery to return to the lungs and begin its trip all over.

In this way, the blood moves in a circle and that is why we speak of the *circulatory system* and of *blood circulation*. The right ventricle is comparatively thin walled because it has to drive the blood only to the lungs and back (the *pulmonary circulation*). The left ventricle has much thicker walls since it must drive the blood through all the remainder of the body and back (the *systemic circulation*). Both ventricles contract simultaneously so that the two circulations are synchronized.

You mustn't suppose, now, that all the hemoglobin of the blood is converted to oxyhemoglobin at any one time, or that all is converted back to hemoglobin at another; that we are full of oxygen at one moment, and empty the next.

The individual hemoglobin molecule switches to oxyhemoglobin in the lung and back to hemoglobin in the tissues, but the situation in the blood stream as a whole remains constant. Some red cells are always in the lung picking up oxygen. Others are always in the tissues unloading oxygen. There are always more red cells waiting their turn in the lung capillaries, waiting to pick up oxygen. There are always more red cells with oxygen crowding behind the ones that have lost their oxygen in the tissues.

You can see what this means by picturing freight cars carrying loads of coal from a mine to a factory. The individual freight car goes to the factory loaded with coal and returns without coal, but there are always a number going one way and a number the other, so that on the whole the mine is supplying a constant flow of coal and the factory is receiving that constant flow regardless of the ups and downs of the individual freight cars.

Blood which is loaded with oxygen and which has most or all of its hemoglobin present as oxyhemoglobin is called *arterial blood*. It is called this because such blood is usually found in arteries, where it is moving away from the heart and has not yet reached the oxygen-hungry tissues. (An exception is the blood in the pulmonary artery which has returned from the tissues and is now traveling toward the lungs.)

Blood which is stripped of its oxygen and carries little or no oxyhemoglobin is called *venous blood*. As its name indicates, it is usually found in the veins, which are carrying blood back to the heart after having passed through the oxygen-hungry tissues. (Again, an exception is the blood in the pulmonary vein, which is fresh from the lung.)

Arterial and venous blood differ in other ways than just in oxygen content. For instance, they aren't the same color. Arterial blood is bright and venous blood is bluish. It is the arterial color that is familiar to us as "the color of blood," because that is what we see when we bleed. Even if a vein were cut and venous blood were coming out of the wound, the blood would turn arterial as soon as it hit the air. It would pick up oxygen quickly and show the bright red of oxyhemoglobin at once.

If you want a glimpse of real venous blood (and are fair-skinned), take a look at the veins that run down the back of your hand or on the inner surface of your wrist. It should be bluish, but you are looking at the veins through a layer of skin which usually contains a certain amount of a yellow pigment called carotene. The addition of yellow gives the veins a greenish tinge.

It is oxyhemoglobin showing through the semi-transparent skin that gives fair-skinned people a rosy complexion. Where the skin is particularly thin, as on the lips or in the mouth, the color is actually red.

Vaso dilatation in the skin increases the redness by allowing more blood to enter the capillaries. This causes the redness about an infected area, or the red mark that follows a slap, or the redness of a blush.

When the oxygen supply is cut off so that the amount of oxyhemoglobin declines, the amount of redness in the skin also declines. In fact, the color of hemoglobin itself begins to show up and the complexion gains a bluish tinge. This shows up in people who have been choked and it is called *cyanosis*, from a Greek word for "blue."

Chapter 4

Breakdowns on the Oxygen Route

As FAR as the normal atmosphere is concerned, hemoglobin is specific for oxygen. That is, it isn't in the least bothered by the presence of the other gases found in air under ordinary circumstances; by nitrogen, carbon dioxide, water vapor or argon. It concentrates on picking up the oxygen molecules only.

However, there are gases which can interfere if present.

For instance, if carbon or a carbon-containing material, such as coal or gasoline, is burned under conditions where oxygen is in rather short supply, a certain quantity of *carbon monoxide* is formed. Carbon monoxide has a molecule made up of one atom of carbon and one of oxygen. With oxygen in good supply, carbon dioxide is formed. It has a molecule made up of an atom of carbon and two of oxygen.

Carbon monoxide is a rather active substance. It will combine with oxygen, burning in the process and changing into the less active and more satisfied carbon dioxide. Carbon monoxide is active enough to combine with substances other than oxygen, too; with iron, for example.

If there is a small quantity of carbon monoxide in the air, it will be drawn into the lungs and some of the carbon monoxide molecules will drift across the various membranes and into the blood. Once in the blood, the carbon monoxide molecule will attach itself to the iron atom in a molecule of hemoglobin.

Any hemoglobin molecule which is carrying carbon monoxide instead of oxygen is useless as far as respiration is concerned. If only a small percentage of hemoglobin is put out of action this way, the results are not serious because the body carries more hemoglobin than it absolutely needs. (After all, you can give a pint of blood to the Red Cross almost any time and never miss it.) However, carbon monoxide has a nasty habit which makes it particularly dangerous. Once it has attached itself to the iron atoms in hemoglobin, it holds on tightly. It doesn't come loose again on small provocation as does the oxygen molecule.

The result is that when the blood works its way through the tissues and returns to the lungs, it returns with just about all the carbon monoxide hemoglobin intact. If there is still some carbon monoxide in the air, more hemoglobin molecules pick it up and they're stuck, too.

The process is cumulative. Before long, even though the carbon monoxide content of the air remains small, a large part of the hemoglobin in the blood is circulating uselessly. Tied up with carbon monoxide, it can't pick up oxygen, and the body is slowly asphyxiated. If there were only ½ per cent carbon monoxide in the air, the result would be fatal in less than half an hour.

That is why poorly ventilated coal furnaces can be dangerous; and why deaths occur when an automobile engine is allowed to run in a closed garage. Cooking gas often contains carbon monoxide and is dangerous for that reason. Carbon monoxide hemoglobin is cherry-red in color and people who die of monoxide poisoning have characteristically flushed complexions.

If a person is suffering from carbon monoxide poisoning but is not yet dead, he should be removed to a place where the air is fresh and given artificial respiration or, if possible, placed in an oxygen tent. Carbon monoxide will break away from hemoglobin slowly and if no other carbon monoxide molecules are waiting to take their place, there's always a chance that the red blood cells will be restored to usefulness before suffocation has gone all the way.

The iron atom, when forming a part of a compound, can exist in one of two forms; as *ferrous ion* or as *ferric ion*. These differ in the amount of electric charge present. The ferrous ion has a double positive charge; the ferric ion a triple positive charge.

In hemoglobin, iron is present as ferrous ion and adding an oxygen molecule doesn't change that. In oxyhemoglobin, the iron atoms are still present as ferrous ion. In a way, this is surprising because the ferrous ion is less stable than the ferric and has a tendency to change over to the latter in the presence of oxygen.

It becomes less surprising if we look more closely. The ferrous ion of hemoglobin is indeed converted to ferric ion in the presence of oxygen and this is happening constantly in the blood. The change from ferrous ion to ferric ion is an example of a type of chemical change known as an *oxidation*. The oxidized hemoglobin that results is called *methemoglobin*. Fortunately, there is a substance present in blood which is capable of changing the ferric ion, as quickly as it is formed, back to ferrous ion. The change from a ferric ion back to a ferrous ion is an example of a type of chemical reaction known as a *reduction*. For that reason, the substance that changes ferric ion to ferrous is called *methemoglobin reductase*.

The reason why the body must see to it that the ferrous ion in hemoglobin stays ferrous ion is that once it is converted to ferric ion, it can no longer pick up oxygen. As far as respiration is concerned, methemoglobin is useless to the body. This is an example of the narrow basis of life. One extra positive charge on the iron atoms and we are dead—an extra charge, moreover, that is continually in danger of being added and that the body must fight off by means of a special mechanism. The fact that the body does develop tricks, dodges and devices for keeping its internal environment favorable doesn't mean that it has broadened the base for life. After all, an acrobat may grow highly skilled at walking the tightrope but that never makes the tightrope a single quarter-inch wider.

Sometimes children are born with a defect in their methemoglobin reductase system. They cannot completely reverse the formation of methemoglobin in their blood and they go through life with anywhere from 10 to 45 per cent of their hemoglobin in the useless methemoglobin state. This does not necessarily prevent them from leading a fairly normal life, but often there is difficulty in breathing after muscular effort (when more oxygen is needed and the body can less afford a hemoglobin shortage). This condition is called *congenital methemoglobinemia*.

(The word "congenital" comes from Latin words meaning "born together with" and applies to diseases or disorders present in an individual from the moment of birth. The ending "emia" is used to refer to something in the blood that should not normally be there, so that "methemoglobinemia" means "an abnormal amount of methemoglobin in the blood." The use of Latin and Greek in forming medical and scientific terms is not an attempt on the part of doctors and scientists to be obscure. It dates back to the time when Latin and Greek were the learned languages of Europe, understood and spoken by all scholars. The system is still used today, when few scientists understand Latin or Greek properly, because the international character of science makes it necessary to use words that will be understood equally well—or equally poorly—by men of all nations.)

There are a number of chemicals (including some medicines) which, when taken internally, encourage the conversion of hemoglobin to methemoglobin at a rate that outstrips the ability of methemoglobin reductase to take care of matters. This becomes most serious when well water contains small quantities of such chemicals. Adults and older children are not generally disturbed by this though some methemoglobin is formed in their blood. Infants under the age of two years, however, are less capable of fighting off the methemoglobinemia and can be made quite ill as a result.

However, just to show you that things are rarely a simple black and white, let me point out that it is possible for methemoglobin, under certain conditions, to cease being a trouble-maker and to become, instead, a life-saver.

There are some chemicals, you see, that react particularly easily with iron when that metal is in its ferric ion state. Examples are hydrogen cyanide (the gas used to execute criminals in gas chambers) and hydrogen sulfide (the "rotten-egg" gas familiar to anyone who has been in a chemistry laboratory in high-school or college).

Both gases are violently poisonous because they combine with certain essential substances within the cells. These essential substances (*cytochromes*) contain iron atoms in the ferric ion state, and are present in only tiny quantities. Even just a little hydrogen cyanide or hydrogen sulfide will combine with the iron and knock out enough of the cytochromes to put the body out of business.

Now if a person is suffering from such poisoning, but is not yet dead, one form of treatment is to give him such chemicals as will convert some of his hemoglobin to methemoglobin.

Once the hemoglobin atoms are converted to the ferric ion state, they will compete for the hydrogen sulfide or hydrogen cyanide molecules and take some, at least, away from the cytochromes.

The body can spare the small amount of hemoglobin lost in this way, and the *sulfhemoglobin* or *cyanhemoglobin* (formed by the attachment of a sulfide or cyanide group) is comparatively harmless. Meanwhile with the cytochromes back in action, the body has a breathing spell during which it can get rid of the poisons altogether.

Sulfhemoglobin is quite blue in color and people who have developed sulfhemoglobinemia for one reason or another may be quite cyanotic (that is, have a distinctly blue complexion) for as long as two months—till they can get rid of the sulf-hemoglobin, that is—without suffering any particularly bad effects. It must be a frightening phenomenon, though.

Sometimes the breakdown along the oxygen route takes place not because of the presence of a particular gas in the air or a particular chemical in food or drink, but because of a shortage of one of the substances needed for proper respiration.

For one thing, it is possible to have a chronic shortage of oxygen. This happens at high altitudes. Earth's atmosphere thins out with altitude and at a height of two miles, a third of Earth's atmosphere is already below you and the quantity of oxygen you draw in at a single breath is only two-thirds what you would have drawn in at sea level.

People accustomed to sea-level life find themselves short of breath on a high plateau and incapable of sustained effort. Yet there are people, such as the Andean natives in the highlands of Peru and Bolivia, who live all their lives at such altitudes and have all the endurance and physical capacity for work that we have.

They get by because their bodies adapt themselves to the handicap of low oxygen. Their lungs, for instance, are generally larger than ours and their capillaries more highly branched. Furthermore, their blood routinely contains an abnormally high quantity of red cells, up to 8,000,000 per cubic millimeter, so that what oxygen is pulled into the lungs gets more thoroughly sieved out by the blood.

A sea-level individual brought up to a high plateau and forced to remain there for a period of time finds that he gets used to the oxygen shortage gradually. His red-cell-manufac-turing apparatus in his bone marrow, in response to the lower oxygen in the blood that reaches it, turns out additional red cells so that, eventually, the blood becomes a more thorough-going oxygen-carrier.

The condition where an abnormally high number of red cells is to be found in the blood is called *polycythemia* (from Greek words meaning "many cells in blood"). When a person is living on a plateau, such a condition is desirable. At sea level, it is not, because too many red cells, when not absolutely needed, thicken the blood, make it more viscous and interfere with its circulation and function.

This is precisely what can happen if the body's feedback mechanism goes out of order. For instance, a thickening or hardening of the walls of the blood-vessels that feed the bone marrow can result in a chronic shortage of the blood flow through that part of the body. It suffers, therefore, from a chronic shortage of oxygen and naturally starts producing extra quantities of red cells that the body really does not need. This disease, *polycythemia vera,* is a serious one and, eventu-ally, fatal.

Another deficiency leading to trouble may be not in the oxygen supply, but in the hemoglobin supply. Sometimes, for some reason, an individual is deficient in hemoglobin. This may be because there is a shortage of red cells or because the individual red cell is short of hemoglobin, or both.

Whatever the reason, the disorder is termed *anemia* (from Greek words meaning "no blood"). The shortage of hemo-globin cuts down the most obvious property of blood; its color. People with anemia tend to be pale as though some of their blood were indeed missing. Also, with the hemoglobin cut down, the oxygen supply to the body cells is cut down. With less oxygen, less energy can be produced and anemic people grow more easily tired. (At least one patent medicine, in its advertising, calls anemia "tired blood.")

The most common cause of anemia is a lack of iron in the body. Sometimes this state of affairs can be traced back to a lack of sufficient iron in the diet, but often a chemical analysis would seem to show that there is plenty of iron in the diet and that still the body goes short.

The trouble rests with the difficulty of getting iron out of the food in the digestive tract and into the body. Iron atoms contained in simple molecules can pass through the intestinal walls quite easily. Iron in hemoglobin, where it is part of a complicated atom arrangement known as *heme,* is not easily absorbed. Unfortunately, most of the iron in food is combined in the form of heme. For that reason, only about 10 per cent of the iron in food is absorbed into the body; the rest is eliminated with the feces and is wasted.

This seems a rather poor way of running things and it is interesting to speculate on what may have caused this state of affairs.

Life began in the oceans, as I've said, and, by and large, living tissue is made up out of those elements that are common in the ocean. There are three elements which are very common in the Earth's crust generally, but are not all common in the ocean. These are silicon (second most common element), aluminum (the third) and iron (the fourth).

The reason these elements are not common in the ocean is that they appear in the Earth's crust in the form of compounds that are not soluble in water. They are not dissolved by falling rain and rushing rivers and do not enter the ocean except in small amounts.

As a consequence, silicon and aluminum are not to be found among the compounds that make up living tissue. They may occur in small quantities as the result of accidental contamination. Popular legend has it that a human being eats a peck of dirt in his lifetime and there is a lot of silicon-and-aluminum-containing compounds in dirt. These small quantities do not, however, fulfil any vital function. Some microorganisms use silicon dioxide to make tiny outer skeletons with, but this is a special case.

Iron, however, is used in living tissue, but only in small amounts. There are certain absolutely essential compounds that require iron for their working but which need be present only in minute quantity in the cell. These compounds are the cytochromes which I mentioned earlier in connection with cyanide poisoning.

The cytochromes handle oxygen within the cell, helping to combine it with the hydrogen of foodstuffs and thus acting to release the energy that keeps the living tissue functioning. Having passed along one oxygen molecule, a cytochrome molecule picks up another. It passes that along and picks up still another. An individual cytochrome molecule can handle many thousands of oxygen molecules per second. For this reason, it is only necessary to have a small quantity of cytochrome molecules in the cell.

It is as though you were building a brick structure. You might need many thousands of bricks, but you could get along with only two or three bricklayers.

With the exception of certain bacteria, all cells contain cytochromes. The exceptional bacteria are those which get energy from reactions that don't involve oxygen. They are the *anaerobic bacteria,* and an example is the bacterium that causes tetanus.

The cytochromes contained in the cells of a 150-pound male adult require a total of about 0.8 grams of iron for their working. That, as you see, is not really much for the well-being of all that mass of body. Unfortunately, though, we need iron for more than cytochromes. Once organisms became multicellular and a blood stream developed, the iron-containing protein, hemoglobin came into existence. Hemoglobin molecules had to travel out to the lungs (or gills) to pick up oxygen and bring it back to the cells where cytochromes could use it.

The increase in the amount of iron required bcause of this is considerable. Think again about bricklayers building a structure. The structure is small and an adequate pile of bricks is lying within arm's reach, so not many bricklayers are needed. That's analogous to the situation of simple organisms floating or swimming in the ocean. Suppose, though, that the structure is large, the brick supply at hand is inadequate and that bricklayers have to walk to the other end of town to get additional bricks, bringing them back an armful at a time. Obviously, you would have to keep a large quantity of bricklayers busily traveling back and forth carrying bricks if the structure is to go up in a reasonable time.

The later case is the situation in the human body. Vast numbers of hemoglobin molecules must travel to the lungs, pick up four oxygen molecules apiece and carry them back to the cytochrome molecules in the cells. (Muscle tissue contains a supply of *myoglobin,* a molecule which is similar to hemoglobin but is only one-quarter its size and contains only one iron atom to the molecule. Myoglobin acts as a middle-man, taking oxygen from the hemoglobin of the blood and passing it on to the cytochromes within the muscle cells.)

In addition, the body stores some iron in case of future

needs and this is done in the form of a protein molecule called *ferritin*, which occurs in the liver, spleen and bone marrow. Almost one-quarter of the weight of the ferritin molecule is iron.

Now, the total amount of iron in the human body, including hemoglobin, myoglobin and ferritin, is about seven grams. This is still not much, but it is nearly nine times as much as the body would have needed if its size and complexity didn't make a blood stream necessary.

Is it possible then that although our iron requirement is nine times as high per cell as is that of a simple ocean creature, we have not developed an iron-absorption mechanism to match the increased requirement? If so, it would be as though a city had grown to nine times its former size without adding to its transport facilities. It can be no wonder then that iron-deficiency anemia is a constant danger.

The body reacts to this situation by conserving its iron supply and hanging on to what it has tightly.

The danger of natural iron loss comes about when a red cell breaks up. The red cells, do not live forever. A particular red cell will, eventually, wear out, break up and be destroyed. When this happens, the hemogobin molecules that were in the red cell are also broken up. Ninety-five per cent of the hemoglobin molecule is the non-iron-containing portion of the protein. This is called *globin*. Globin is broken down into smaller groups of atoms which may be used to build other proteins or for other purposes. The fate of globin is not particularly important since the body can easily manufacture additional globin as required.

The remaining 5 per cent of the hemoglobin molecule is the iron-containing heme. In addition to the iron atom, the heme is made up of a complicated arrangement of atoms called the *porphyrin ring*. The body disposes of heme by breaking the porphyrin ring and then prying the iron atom loose. The broken ring without the iron atom is an example of a *bile pigment*. (It is called a pigment because these compounds are generally colored. The porphyrin ring itself is colored and molecules containing it are often purplish. The word "porphyrin" comes from a Greek word meaning "purple.")

The bile pigments are various shades of red and green. After being formed they are extracted from the blood by the liver, which discharges them into the intestines as part of the secretion known as *bile,* which the liver is constantly pouring into the intestines. (These broken-porphyrin molecules were first located in the bile and that is how they got their name of "bile pigments.") The bile pigments travel through the intestines and are finally excreted along with the feces. In fact, the color of feces is due to the bile pigment it contains. The body takes no pains to save the porphyrin, any more than it tries to conserve globin. The body can make additional quantities of porphyrin, as required, without trouble.

(It sometimes happens that the duct leading from the liver to the intestine, through which the bile must pass, is obstructed, usually by a gall-stone. When this happens bile-pigment accumulates first in the liver, then in the blood. The greenish color of the accumulating bile pigment shows up in the blood and therefore in the complexion. The condition is known as *obstructive jaundice.* Jaundice can also be caused by other conditions, too, as for instance certain liver diseases and certain disorders involving the too rapid breakdown of red cells.)

There remains the third part of the hemoglobin molecule, the iron atoms themselves. These do not leave the body, but stay where they are and are used over again in the construction of new hemoglobin molecules.

In fact, some scientists suggest that the efficiency with which iron atoms are conserved by the body can be disadvantageous and that the low absorption of iron is not an imperfection in the bodily mechanism but a necessary device to keep too much iron from accumulating. There are people who, for reasons not well understood, absorb abnormally high quantities of iron which then accumulate. Over a period of years, up to 50 grams of excess iron (or seven times the normal amount of iron) may accumulate as ferritin and as another iron-storage protein, *hemosiderin.*

This condition is the opposite of iron-deficiency anemia and is called *hemochromatosis.* It is treated by bleeding the patient once every week or two to drain off some of his iron supply and bring him down closer to normal. (This is one case, anyway, where the old-fashioned medical stand-by of bleeding is useful.)

(It would be interesting to know how the vampire bat, which feeds on blood exclusively and therefore has a high-iron diet, manages to avoid accumulating too much iron. Is its absorption rate very low or does it have a means of getting rid of the iron once absorbed? I have come across no information on the matter.)

The question of how many times iron atoms must be broken off the hemoglobin molecule and then incorporated into a new hemoglobin molecule depends upon how long a red cell remains intact; its lifetime, in other words. The length of life of a red cell was not, as it turned out, particularly easy to determine. Viewed under the microscope, all the red cells look the same; there are no bright young ones or doddering old ones. And yet the red cells don't live forever. Small fragments of broken-up red cells (*hemoconia,* or *blood dust*) are frequently found in blood. These are strained out in the spleen and are absorbed there by large cells called *macrophages*. What are the details of red cell breakup then?

Two possibilities exist. Either a red cell's life depends upon pure chance, so that some might live for minutes, others for weeks and still others for years (depending on how often a particular red cell was banged into the walls of the blood-vessels and sustained damage), or a red cell might have a particular length of life pretty much regardless of the treatment it received.

The truth was reached by making use of isotopes, and this is only one example of thousands of scientific problems that have been settled in the last generation by means of this novel technique.

Most types of atoms occur in several varieties called *isotopes*. The nitrogen atom occurs in two varieties, for instance, which are called *nitrogen-14* and *nitrogen-15*. Of the two, nitrogen-14 is by far the more common. Of all nitrogen atoms, nitrogen-14 makes up 99.64 per cent and nitrogen-15 only 0·36 per cent. The hemoglobin molecule contains about 750 nitrogen atoms all together and of these, two atoms (on the average) are nitrogen-15; the rest are nitrogen-14.

Scientists have learned to separate isotopes and to prepare nitrogen-containing compounds that have an unusually high percentage of nitrogen-15. One such compound is *glycine,* a substance which, when added to the food, is absorbed by the body and incorporated into proteins generally, and into hemoglobin in particular. It may be incorporated intact into the globin portion of the molecule, while pieces of the glycine (including the nitrogen atom it contains) may be incorporated into the heme portion of the molecule as well.

The investigating scientist can tell that the glycine has been incorporated by isolating some of the hemoglobin from a blood sample (easily done), separating the nitrogen atoms from the hemoglobin molecules (also easily done) and then analyzing the nitrogen to determine what percentage of it is nitrogen-15. This is not so easily done, but involves quite a complicated instrument called the *mass spectrograph,* which measures the weight of individual atoms, and can tell a heavier atom, like nitrogen-15, from a slightly lighter twin such as nitrogen-14. If it turns out that the hemoglobin molecule is unusually rich in nitrogen-15, the simplest explanation is that hemoglobin molecules were built up, at least partly, out of the glycine in the diet.

Because an unusual isotope can be followed in this way from compound to compound, it enables us to keep track of the whereabouts and viscissitudes of particular substances during their chemical adventuring in living tissue, much as a label or tag will keep us on the track of a piece of luggage or a package working its way through the railway express system. In fact, compounds containing unusual isotopes are referred to, for this reason, as *tagged compounds.*

Now let's see how tagged glycine can be used to determine the lifetime of a red cell. The tagged glycine is fed to human beings over a period of two days by adding it to their usual food. At intervals, blood samples are taken and the hemoglobin content is analyzed for nitrogen-15. Samples of the feces are taken also and analyzed. For a couple of weeks, the nitrogen-15 content of the hemoglobin rises as the glycine is slowly incorporated into the hemoglobin molecule. The reason for the delay is that a portion of the glycine is incorporated into other proteins first and only enters the hemoglobin after having been sidetracked for a while.

After that first couple of weeks, the nitrogen-15 content of the hemoglobin reaches a peak and holds quite steady for three months or more. At the same time the nitrogen-15 content of the feces remains low and steady. This would indicate that the red cells are not breaking down at random; for if they were, the nitrogen-15 in hemoglobin would start dropping at once after a peak had been reached. Moreover, more and more nitrogen-15 would appear in the bile pigments, which are just broken-down heme molecules, as I've explained. These would appear in the feces, which would therefore show a steadily rising nitrogen-15 content.

Neither of these two things happens. Instead, after about 120 days of quiet, there is the sudden beginning of a decline in the nitrogen-15 of hemoglobin and, simultaneously, there is a sharp rise in the nitrogen-15 of the feces. Apparently, after having survived for about four months all told, the red cells that had been formed during the period when tagged glycine was being fed, all start breaking down more or less together.

For this reason it has been decided that the human red cell has a definite life span which averages about 125 days. Some live a bit longer, some not quite as long, just as human beings might have an average life span of 70 years, while certain individuals may die younger and others live longer. These results, obtained by the use of isotopes, agree with earlier determinations by other, less elegant, methods. A scientific conclusion is always most satisfactory if it is arrived at from two or more directions. Of course, some red cells are being formed every second, and some red cells reach their natural life span and break up every second.

If our average adult has 25,000,000,000,000 (twenty-five trillion) red cells altogether and 1/125 (or 0·8 per cent) of them break up each day, then 200,000,000,000 (two hundred billion) are being destroyed daily, or 2,300,000 each second. Of course, this should not be at all disturbing. The body can, and does, replace the quantity being broken down as fast as they are broken down.

The red cells in other species of animals do not necessarily have the same life span as those of man. The red cells of dogs have a lifetime of only about 107 days, those of the cat and the rabbit only 68 days.

In experimenting with animals it is possible to use *radioactive isotopes*—special isotopes that generally do not exist in nature but which can be manufactured in the laboratory. Radioactive isotopes are unstable and are breaking down continuously, liberating very energetic subatomic particles that can be easily detected by the use of appropriate instruments called *counters*. (The Geiger counter is the one most familiar to the general public.)

Radioactive isotopes can be so easily and delicately detected that only very small quantities need be used. Furthermore, analyzing for them does not involve the expensive and hard-to-handle mass spectrograph. Most isotope work these days involves the use of radioactive isotopes, rather than unusual but non-radioactive isotopes such as nitrogen-15. It is one of the great boons of atomic research that nuclear reactors are capable of producing radioactive isotopes in such quantities that compounds containing them may now be bought quite cheaply, whereas before World War II, they were either unobtainable altogether or, at best, fearfully expensive.

Radioactive isotopes are not used in experiments with human beings except under unusual condtions. The flying subatomic particles released by the isotope as it breaks down can and will damage tissue and produce *radiation sickness* if the dose is high enough. Scientists who work with radioactive isotopes must keep rigid track of the radiation to which they are exposed and never allow it to exceed certain safe limits in any unit of time. But this is no worse, after all, than the case of the bacteriologist who must take care not to be infected by the specimens he studies or, for that matter, the butcher who must keep his fingers out of the way of his cleaver.

If the body hangs on to the iron it possesses and if there is at least a small amount of iron absorbed from the food, why should anyone worry about anemia? Well, the adult male generally need not. Once he has piled up an adequate supply of iron he is reasonably set up for the future in that respect, if all continues well.

Of course, everything need not continue well. If a man is hurt and loses blood (*hemorrhage*), that blood and all it contains, including the iron atoms, must be made up. The iron atoms in the body's ferritin supply come in handy then, but even so dietary iron is necessary, if only to rebuild the ferritin supply.

The situation with women under fifty is less satisfactory. A man may be lucky or careful and be safe from losing blood, but a woman loses a quantity of blood regularly (usually every four weeks) as a result of the menstrual flow. Her need for iron in the diet is thus greater than that of a man's. The consequence is that simple iron-deficiency anemia is much more common among women (especially young women who, on top of everything else, are likely to be trying to keep slim by self-designed and unsupervised diets which will be short in vitamins, minerals and everything but calories) than among men.

The problem of iron-deficiency becomes particularly crucial during pregnancy. To be sure the menstrual flow stops during pregnancy, but now a baby is being built up within the woman's body; a baby who is obtaining all its substance from its mother, including what is necessary for its manufacture of a blood supply. Not only must iron for the infant's blood be supplied by the mother (even at the cost of dangerously stripping the expectant mother's own blood), but also a quantity of additional iron to serve the child as a reserve supply during the very first stages of independent life after birth. The loss of iron to the growing fetus is about 60 per cent greater than the amount that would have been lost in menstruation during the nine-month period if the woman had not been pregnant. It is understandable then that "iron pills," containing inorganic iron compounds that are easily absorbed, are almost routinely prescribed during pregnancy.

A child is born not only with the reserve iron supply just mentioned but with an abnormally high concentration of red cells in its blood, a mild polycythemia, in other words. This may be the result of the shortage of oxygen from which the baby suffers before birth. After all, it is out of contact with air itself while it is within the womb and must get along only on the oxygen that leaks across from the mother's blood stream.

In any case, both the iron reserve and the extra red cells come in handy during the first few months of the child's life, when it is growing and must be increasing its red cell supply without having much iron in the diet. Milk, which is likely to be its exclusive food item for several months, is very poor in iron. That is one of its few defects. (Another is that, unless it is specially treated, it is also very poor in vitamin D.) As early as possible, therefore, eggs or cereal should be added to the infant's diet. These have enough iron to meet the baby's needs.

A girl will then continue to need a good iron supply in the diet until the menopause is reached. A boy will need one as long as he is growing and in fact his maximum needs are in young adolescence at the age of fifteen or sixteen.

Chapter 5

The Red Vitamin

SOMETIMES it is not the body's manufacture of hemoglobin that hits a snag, but the manufacture of the red cell itself; of the "bag" that holds the hemoglobin. This "bag" is called the *stroma*. Red cells placed in distilled water will burst after a time, and the hemoglobin will escape. The empty husk of the red cell remains behind and is given the dramatic name of a red cell "ghost." Stroma material probably penetrates the interior of the cell, too, setting up partitions. It is sometimes possible to treat a red cell so that part of the hemoglobin spills out while the remainder stays put, apparently held back by those thin stroma partitions that have managed to hold firm.

Where there is interference with stroma manufacture, the red cells that are formed are abnormal in appearance and break down too quickly. The half-life of the cell is only about 40 days instead of the normal 125 days. Each cell has all the hemoglobin it ought to have; if anything, it has more than normal quantities. Then, too, the red cells are larger than normal (macrocytes). The trouble, however, is that the number of cells is low and gets constantly lower, generally reaching counts of less than 2,500,000 per cubic millimeter.

Such a condition is called *pernicious anemia*. One of the meanings of "pernicious" is "fatal" and that's what this kind of anemia was until 1926. Ordinary iron-deficiency anemia could be cured by taking a few iron pills now and then, but pernicious anemia was as fatal as a bullet through the heart (though not as quickly, as it took two to five years to run its course).

In 1926, two physicians at Harvard University, named G. R. Minot and W. P. Murphy, decided to feed liver to patients with pernicious anemia. You may ask, why liver? Well, some years earlier a University of California scientist named G. H. Whipple had produced anemia in dogs by deliberately bleeding them and had then tested various foods to see which would most quickly help the dogs get back to normal. It turned out liver did the best job. Of course, the dog's trouble was not pernicious anemia, but anemia due to hemorrhage. Still, Minot and Murphy had nothing to lose. Liver was an edible food and the patients were facing sure death; so they tried it.

It worked. The patients improved almost at once. To be sure, the patients had to keep on eating sizable portions of liver at periodic intervals. If they stopped doing so for any length of time, the disease started taking hold again. Still, faced with an alternative of eating liver often or of dying by inches, the choice seems clear.

In 1934, Minot, Murphy and Whipple shared the Nobel Prize in Medicine for this accomplishment.

Things, however, could not be and were not allowed to remain at this point, satisfactory though it was in comparison with the earlier situation. What was it in liver that restored pernicious anemia patients to normal? Beginning in 1927, E. J. Cohn, along with Minot and others at Harvard, started fractionating liver in an attempt to concentrate the *anti-pernicious anemia factor.*

To begin with, a quantity of raw liver was minced up fine (that is, *homogenized*). The minced tissue was immersed in water adjusted to a particular acidity and the mixture was stirred for a period of time. Some of the liver material dissolved in the water and some did not.

The watery solution was filtered off and both the solution and the insoluble material that was left behind were separately tested by feeding small quantities to a pernicious anemia patient and then taking blood samples at intervals to see whether there followed an increase in immature red cells (called *reticulocytes*). Such a "reticulocyte response" would indicate the presence of the anti-pernicious anemia factor.

When this was done, the water solution, or *liver extract,* was found to have the factor present, while the insoluble portion of the liver had little or none. The insoluble portion could therefore be discarded and further work concentrated upon the liver extract alone.

(Later on, the presence or absence of the factor was determined by injecting small quantities of various liver fractions into the veins. This was a much more sensitive test than that of adding it to food as smaller portions of the fractions were used up in testing and larger amounts left behind for further purification. Attempts were also made to find a way to use animals as test subjects rather than human patients, since pernicious anemia is a comparatively rare disease, but without success.)

The liver extract was next heated. The effect of the heat was to coagulate some of the protein that was in the solution and cause it to come out of solution. The factor remained in solution.

After filtration (to get rid of the coagulated protein), the solution was treated with ether. The ether does not mix with water but forms a separate layer of liquid floating on top of the water. When the two layers are temporarily mixed by vigorous shaking, some of the substances still in the water, which are even more soluble in ether, pass into the ether layer. The ether layer is then separated off and discarded, for it was found that the anti-pernicious anemia factor remained in the water.

The solution was then placed in a collodion bag and bathed in distilled water. Collodion acts as a semi-permeable membrane through which fairly small molecules, such as those of the factor, will pass, while larger ones will remain behind. Such a procedure is called *dialysis.* To the material that has passed through the bag (the *dialysate*) various chemicals are next added, which will combine with various substances still present (but not with the factor), forming insoluble compounds that come out of solution and can be removed.

By such methods, together with some I haven't mentioned, the search is gradually but steadily narrowed, and the anti-pernicious anemia factor is prepared in purer and purer form. Naturally, the procedure is tedious. It had to be hit-or-miss (except that experienced research men, owing to their knowledge of chemical and physical principles usually have a flair for choosing procedures that have a better than even chance to work); blind alleys had to be explored; attempts of one sort or another had to be repeated and repeated.

Still in 1930, after three years of work, Cohn and his co-workers had a liver fraction that was effective in combatting pernicious anemia in 140 milligram quantities. Such a fraction was at least a hundred times more powerful than the original liver. Pernicious anemia patients treated with small quantities of such an extract were thus liberated from slavery to liver itself as a compulsory part of the diet.

Work could not go much further so long as the reactions of pernicious anemia patients were the only way the anti-pernicious anemia factor could be detected. What with the unavoidable losses at each stage of purification, and the additional losses through testing, quantities were getting too small to work with. Fortunately, in the 1940's, scientists at the laboratories of Merck and Co., Inc. discovered that a small quantity of the factor (an extremely small quantity, indeed, one measured in *micromicrograms;* that is, millionths of a millionth of a gram) would accelerate the growth rate of certain bacteria.

This is not really very surprising, even though bacteria don't have red cells. It was early suspected that the anti-pernicious anemia factor was a vitamin. When vitamins were first discovered, to backtrack a little, they were known only as mysterious substances of unknown composition which were present in food in small amounts and which were necessary to human health and well-being. Two vitamins were at first recognized: "vitamin A" which was soluble in fat but not in water, and "vitamin B" which was soluble in water but not in fat. Further investigation showed that "vitamin B" was actually a mixture of many compounds and this mixture was termed the *B vitamin complex.*

Individual members of the complex were termed vitamin B_1, vitamin B_2 and so on. Eventually, when the chemical structures of the individual vitamins were determined, they were given names. For instance, vitamin B_1 is now called thiamin and vitamin B_2 riboflavin.

One thing all the B vitamins have in common is this: they are each needed for the proper chemical functioning of all known cells; animal, plant and bacterial. If the cell cannot make its own, it must depend for its supply on the food it lives on.

The anti-pernicious anemia factor behaved like a B vitamin and it was given the name *vitamin B12*. Like the other B vitamins, it is needed in all cells. In the human body, a shortage of vitamin B12 happens to make itself most seriously felt in the inability to manufacture red cells, but this is just the visible symptom. The more fundamental trouble is that some bit of body chemistry is upset in every cell. It is upset in bacterial cells too, and bacteria which can't make their own cannot grow if there is none in the nutrient medium on which they feed. If vitamin B12 is added to the medium, then they begin to grow and that is the basis for the use of bacteria in detecting the anti-pernicious anemia factor.

By 1948, with the help of this new technique, pure vitamin B12 was finally obtained in tiny quantities. This was accomplished almost simultaneously by two independent lines of research, one at Merck and Co. in America, and one at a set of laboratories in England.

Vitamin B12 turned out to be a red substance. This red color was unusual and at first the investigating scientists were sure that the color belonged to an impurity. However, wherever the vitamin B12 went during the process of purification, the red color went, too.

Then a surprising thing came to pass. The color resembled somewhat the color of certain known compounds containing the element, *cobalt*. (Cobalt is a metal with properties very like those of iron.) This seemed just a coincidence because cobalt had never been found in any substance isolated from living tissue. Nevertheless a small quantity of vitamin B12 was ashed (that is, heated slowly but intensely, until everything burnable was burnt off and only a bit of mineral residue was left behind). The ash was analyzed and it contained cobalt! Again, this was determined in 1948 in England and in the United States simultaneously.

Since vitamin B12 is necessary to the functioning of all cells and since cobalt is part of the vitamin, it meant that cobalt joined the list of those elements necessary to life. Because it is necessary in very small quantities, it is called an *essential trace element*. In our average adult male, there is probably not more than 12 milligrams of cobalt. This is equivalent to a cube of cobalt with sides only a trifle over a millimeter. It would seem a completely insignificant amount, yet it is essential to life.

Of course, 12 milligrams is not as small a quantity as you might think. In that 12 milligrams there are present somewhat more than 100,000,000,000,000,000,000 (a hundred million trillion) atoms. If this were spread evenly among the various cells in the human body, there would be enough to supply each cell with hundreds of thousands of cobalt atoms.

In dealing with vitamin B_{12}, it was found that several closely related but distinct substances could be prepared. These were termed vitamin B_{12a}, vitamin B_{12b} and so on. Altogether they were given the name of *cobalamines* from the fact that they contained cobalt. (The "t" of "cobalt" was left out for the sake of euphony.) Vitamin B_{12}, as it occurs in the body, also contains the cyanide group, so it was named *cyanocobalamine*. Cyanide is poisonous, of course, but too little is present in cyanocobalamine to do us harm and what little there is, is held so tightly to the rest of the molecule that it can't in any case get loose to attach itself damagingly to iron atoms.

As soon as cyanocobalamine was isolated, attempts were made to determine its structure. The cobalt was found at once, of course, but what of the other atoms in the molecule? There were many of these and they were arranged in a particularly complicated pattern; so complicated that it took an additional eight years to find the answer.

To begin with, the molecule of cyanocobalamine was treated with strong chemicals in order to break it into smaller fragments. The much simpler structure of the individual fragments was determined. As a result of this, chemists could say by the early 1950's, with fair certainty, that a molecule of cyanocobalamine contained 63 carbon atoms, 88 hydrogen atoms, 14 oxygen atoms, 14 nitrogen atoms, 1 phosphorus atom and 1 cobalt atom. They could arrange most of the atoms into small patterns, but the overall model of the entire molecule remained obscure.

Dr. Dorothy Hodgkin of Oxford set to work observing the way beams of x-rays behaved when they passed through crystals of cyanocobalamine. Some of the x-rays were bent (*diffracted*) as they passed through. The manner in which they were bent—that is, by how much and in what directions

—could be determined by allowing the beam to fall on a photographic plate after it had passed through the crystals. If the crystals had not been there, there would be one spot of blackening where the beam would hit. With the crystals in the way, there would still be that blackening, but in addition there would be blackened dots elsewhere on the plate, representing the spots where x-rays had struck after being bent out of their straight-line flight.

From the position of these scattered dots one could build up a picture of the *electron density* of the molecule. That is, it was possible to tell at which point in the molecule there was a high probability of finding an electron and at which point a low probability. (*Electrons* are tiny particles, much smaller than atoms, that are to be found within all atoms and which form part of their structure.) Lines could then be drawn, representing all points of equal electron density, much as lines can be drawn on a weather chart to represent all points at a certain temperature or at a certain barometric pressure. The lines of electron density give a kind of ghostly picture of the atoms in the proper arrangement within the molecule. From that and from what was already known of the structure of various pieces of the molecule, the entire structure could be determined.

The one catch is that the calculation of electron densities from the x-ray diffraction picture is long, tedious and quite a complicated affair. Dr. Hodgkin cut that Gordian knot by making use of a modern computer. The data was fed to the National Bureau of Standards Western Automatic Computer (SWAC) and the answers tumbled out.

As a result, the formula of cyanocobalamine was determined in 1956. It was found to consist of a lop-sided porphyrin ring such as that found in heme, (lop-sided because one atom of the ring was missing) and in the center of the ring, in place of heme's iron atom, there was a cobalt atom. Attached to the ring at various points were a number of atom groups that were more complicated than similar groups present in heme.

The molecule is far too complicated to be synthesized in the laboratory just yet, but ample supplies for medical purposes can be obtained from liver. (It is the liver that stores excess quantities of vitamins during periods of good diet, for use during lean periods, and it is for this reason that liver was helpful in pernicious anemia, and is a useful item in the diets of even healthy people.) Nowadays, most commercial multi-vitamin prepartions contain small quantities of cyanocobalamine.

One puzzle about cyanocobalamine arises from the fact that the body needs it in such small quantities. As far as the other B vitamins are concerned, the body requires a milligram a day or more. As for cyanocobalamine, on the other hand, one or two micrograms a day (a thousandth the usual B vitamin quantity) is sufficient.

But if this is so, you see, why should there ever be pernicious anemia? The vitamin is present in many foods; in very small quantity, to be sure, but in sufficient amounts to make up this tiny need of ours. In fact, it is practically impossible to figure out a normal diet that wouldn't have enough cyanocobalamine in it.

To show what I mean, consider another type of anemia, one resulting from a shortage of copper in the diet. Copper, like cobalt, is an essential trace element. Copper forms part of the molecules of certain proteins, called *enzymes,* which are needed in small quantities by the body to control various necessary chemical reactions. Some of these copper-containing enzymes have been isolated. One, which has not yet been isolated, is needed by the body to control some chemical reaction (not yet identified) which enables the body's iron supply to be properly handled. In the absence of copper, the iron atoms are not used properly, a hemoglobin shortage develops and the result is *copper-deficiency anemia.* Yet such is the widespread occurrence of minute quantities of copper in the diet that copper-deficiency anemia is never observed in humans. The only way scientists can study it at all is to use animals, such as young dogs, and feed them for months on special diets from which as much copper as possible has been painstakingly removed.

Well, why isn't it the same with pernicious anemia, which, after all, is a kind of "cobalt-deficiency anemia"? To make it more puzzling, many bacteria, including those particular bacteria that live in our intestines, can make cyanocobalamine out of simpler substances. For that reason, even if the cobalt in food were perhaps not in the form of cyanocobalamine (and therefore unusable by us), bacteria would put it into that form. They do exactly that and we generally have more than we can use so that some of it does not get absorbed through the intestinal wall but instead passes clear through the alimentary canal and is excreted with the feces.

This actually, is the key to the mystery. Having the cyanocobalamine in the intestines is not the same as having it in the body. Under the best of circumstances, in the most normal individuals, not much of this large molecule (the other B vitamins all have molecules that are considerably smaller) is absorbed into the body; though enough is absorbed for our needs. In patients with pernicious anemia, hardly any cyanocobalamine is absorbed. This shows up in the fact that the feces of pernicious anemia patients contain more cyanocobalamine (for want of which they are dying) than do the feces of normal people.

It is the absorption of cyanocobalamine that is at fault, not the mere fact of its presence or absence in food. This also shows up in the treatment of pernicious anemia. Two micrograms of cyanocobalamine injected into the blood will produce a noticeable reticulocyte response. It takes nearly a hundred times as much, fed by mouth, to get the same result. In normal individuals, the same small amount is almost as effective by mouth as by injection.

At a comparatively early stage in the game, interest was centered on the stomach secretions of pernicious anemia patients. Ordinarily, the *gastric juice* secreted by the stomach is rich in hydrochloric acid. This is a strong acid and the gastric juice is by far the most acid fluid in the body. This acid is useful (despite the advertisements of people who manufacture antacid pills) because it helps digest the stomach contents and because it is necessary for the workings of the stomach's most important digestive enzyme. In rare instances, hydrochloric acid is not found in the gastric juice, and such a condition is called *achlorhydria*. Without hydrochloric acid, digestion in the stomach is cut down, but this is made up for in the remainder of the alimentary tract, so that if nothing else is wrong with a person, achlorhydria is not a serious condition.

However, patients with pernicious anemia almost invariably have achlorhydria and so the gastric juice received considerable attention. It was found, for instance, that meat which had been treated with normal gastric juice is ten times as effective in eliciting a reticulocyte response as is untreated meat. There was obviously something in the gastric juice (aside from the acid) that helped in the absorption of the vitamin.

In 1929, the American investigator, W. B. Castle, named this gastric substance *intrinsic factor*. "Intrinsic," used in this sense, refers to something located within the body. Cyanocobalamine, which at that time was just as mysterious a substance as the gastric substance, was sometimes called *extrinsic factor* because it was located in the food; outside the body, in other words.

Intrinsic factor is now known to be a small protein molecule, about one-quarter the size of the hemoglobin molecule. It contains as part of its molecule certain atom groupings related to those found in sugar molecules. Such a sugar-containing protein is called a *mucoprotein*.

Although pernicious anemia is no longer a killer and is, in fact, quite easily controlled, there are many questions still remaining that profoundly interest the scientist. What is the exact structure of intrinsic factor? How does it help the cyanocobalamine pass through the intestinal wall? Once inside the body, how does cyanocobalamine participate in body chemistry and why is it needed in such small amounts? Exactly how does its absence interfere with stroma manufacture?

In the story of science, chapters may be ended but the book itself has no end.

I feel I ought to point out here that the history of pernicious anemia shows how useful experiments on live animals can be. It is not pleasant to bleed a dog severely just to see how it goes about replacing its lost blood. Even with every care to avoid pain and discomfort, and with every effort to perform the experiment as humanely as possible, Dr. Whipple could not have enjoyed doing the work for which he obtained the Nobel Prize. But it was *necessary* work. As a result of it, a disease that had been a sure killer was brought under control and a line of investigation was initiated that has taught us much about the body so that incalculable beneficial results await us yet in the future. If those experiments on dogs had not been conducted, Minot and Murphy might still have happened to feed liver to their patients but, on the other hand, they might not, and pernicious anemia might still be a killer today.

Chapter 6

A Gift of Blood

SEVERAL THINGS CAN GO WRONG with red cells through no fault of their own but, rather, through the introduction of foreign substances into the blood stream. For instance, some snake poisons (as well as the venom of scorpions and centipedes) contain chemicals which break up some of the compounds in the stroma of red cells. The stroma is ruptured as a result and the hemoglobin is poured out into the blood plasma. The colorless stroma is left behind and is referred to dramatically as a *red cell ghost*.

This phenomenon of red cell rupture and breakup is called *hemolysis,* and it can also be caused by parasites which invade the red cell, multiply within it and, eventually, break it. The most common disease involving such a parasite is malaria.

Another and equally dangerous red cell aberration can also be induced from outside. Substances can be introduced into the blood stream that will cause red cells to clump together, that is to *agglutinate*. Any substance capable of bringing this about is an *agglutinin*. The danger of agglutination is obvious. Agglutinated red cells cannot do their job and, worse, clumps of red cells will plug the smaller vessels. Blockage of a strategic vessel, in the brain, for instance, can cause paralysis or even death.

The most important agglutinins occur in blood itself, and it is these blood agglutinins which raise most of the problems in connection with the transfer of blood (i.e. *transfusion*) from one person to another.

As I said in the first chapter, mankind must have realized from prehistoric times that loss of blood led to death. In recent centuries there have been occasions when some imaginative (or desperate) doctor would try to remedy the loss of blood by introducing new blood into the patient's veins from some outside source, usually from some animal such as a sheep or a goat. This did no good.

Even when attempts were made to use the blood of a second human being to save the life of the first, results were not always good. Sometimes the patient lived; often, he died the faster. Understanding of why this should be so had to await the twentieth century.

The puzzle was solved, beginning with the work of the Austrian physiologist, Karl Landsteiner, in 1901. He divided human beings into three groups (a fourth was added in 1902), according to the manner in which their blood agglutinated other blood or was agglutinated by other blood.

The necessity for such a division lies in the fact that human blood plasma may contain one or another of two different agglutinins. The stroma of human red cells may, analogously, contain one or another of two different compounds with which the agglutinins may combine to cause red cell clumping. These stroma compounds are called *agglutinogens*.

The two agglutinogens are termed simply *A substance* and *B substance*. The red cells of a particular individual may all contain A substance only, or B substance only, or both, or neither. There are your four groups.

In addition, the plasma of a particular human being may contain the agglutinin that causes red cells containing A substance to agglutinate. This agglutinin is specific; that is, it will react only with A substance, not at all with B substance. The agglutinin is called *anti-A*. Alternatively, the plasma may contain the other agglutin, which is specific for B substance only, and is called *anti-B*, or it may contain both agglutinins, or neither. Again four groups.

This double listing of four groups is not independent, since a person possessing a certain agglutinogen in his red cells can only have a certain agglutinin in his plasma. Each individual has in his plasma only those agglutinins which will not combine with the agglutinogens in his red cells. Any other arrangement would make life impossible.

For instance, a person with B substance in his red cells would invariably have anti-A in his plasma; the anti-A having no effect at all on his B cells. Similarly, a person whose red cells contained A substance would have anti-B in his plasma. A person with neither A substance nor B substance in his red cells would have both anti-A and anti-B in his plasma. Finally, a person with both A substance and B substance in his red cells would have neither anti-A nor anti-B in his plasma.

(Actually, blood cells without either A or B substance do contain a similar substance called *H substance,* but there are no "anti-H" agglutinins and so this substance can be ignored.)

This can be summarized as follows:

agglutinogen in the red cell	agglutinin in the plasma
none	anti-A and anti-B
A	anti-B
B	anti-A
A and B	none

On the basis of the situation in the table above, human beings are divided into four groups. Three of the groups are those human beings of *blood type A, blood type B,* and *blood type AB,* depending on the nature of the agglutinogens in their red cells. People without either A or B substance in their red cells belong to *blood type O.*

These groups are of equal size. In the United States 44·4 per cent of the population are of blood group O and 39·5 per cent of blood group A. Together, they account for five-sixths of the population. Those of blood group B come to 11·8 per cent and those of AB to only 4·2 per cent.

Ideally, a patient who needs blood ought to be given blood only from a donor belonging to the same blood group. This limits the possibilities especially for those with the "minority groups," B and AB. Suppose for instance that a patient is of blood type AB and that ten members of the hospital staff voluntarily offer to give him blood. The chances are three to two that not one of those ten will be of blood type AB. It would be disastrous, then, for the patient if the transfusion rules could not be made more liberal. Fortunately, they can.

Suppose, for instance, that a pint of blood from a blood-donor of blood type B is transfused into the veins of a patient of blood type A. The donated blood is, roughly half red cells and half plasma and each half is a source of possible trouble because of the blood type incompatibility.

First, the plasma of the B blood-donor contains anti-A, while the A patient's red cells contain A substance. The donor's plasma might therefore agglutinate the patient's red cells. This, however, is not as serious a danger as it sounds. Generally, the concentration of agglutinins in plasma is not high and the half-pint of plasma donated does not introduce much of the agglutinin into the patient's blood stream. Furthermore, the donor's plasma is quickly mixed with and dispersed into the much greater volume of the patient's own plasma so that the amount of anti-A is thinned out even further, to the point where its effect on the patient's red cells can be ignored.

But there is the second danger. The donor's red cells, in the case we are considering, contain B substance. Since the patient is of blood type A, his plasma contains anti-B. Now it is the patient's agglutinins, the agglutinins of an entire blood stream and not of a half-pint only, that are involved. The donor's red cells are greeted by an overwhelming quantity of anti-B as soon as they get into the patient's blood stream and they agglutinate. The donated red cell clumps collect in the kidney and elsewhere and, in doing so, will certainly harm the patient and will probably kill him.

So you see, in considering transfusion dangers, we must check on the donor's red cells (not his plasma) and on the patient's plasma (not his red cells).

Begin, for instance, with a donor of blood type O. His red cells contain neither A substance nor B substance and will not agglutinate in any kind of blood. Blood type O can therefore be transfused into anyone without very much fear of red cell agglutination. The anti-A and anti-B in the donor's plasma will not, usually, do any harm to anyone. A person of blood type O is therefore a *universal donor*. It is for this reason that, during World War II and the Korean war, when quantities of blood were needed on the battlefield, donations of O blood were particularly desirable.

A donor of blood type A cannot give blood to any patient with anti-A in his plasma. This means that such a donor can give blood to a patient of blood type A or AB, but not to a patient of blood type O or B.

Similarly, a donor of blood type B cannot give blood to any patient with anti-B in his plasma. He can therefore only give blood to patients of blood type B or AB, but not to patients of blood type O or A.

A donor of blood type AB cannot give blood to any patient with either anti-A or anti-B in his plasma. He can therefore only give blood to a patient of blood type AB.

From the patient's point of view, it works out like this. A patient with blood type AB can receive blood from anyone. (So the AB patient with whom we started this discussion is not as badly off as we would have thought. He doesn't need to find another AB. He can take anyone's blood.) A patient with blood type A can receive blood only from a donor of blood type A or O. A patient with blood type B can receive blood only from a donor of blood type B or O. A patient with blood type O can receive blood only from a donor of blood type O.

The whole scheme can be shown in a simple diagram, with arrows giving the direction of permissible transfusions, as follows:

Obviously, when transfusions are involved, it is necessary to know the blood type of both the patient and the donor. Fortunately it is easy and quick to determine the blood type from a drop of blood, provided the doctor or lab technician has a supply of anti-A and anti-B (prepared from blood of known type) and is experienced in the business. The drop of blood from the person being tested (taken by pricking a finger or an ear-lobe) is thinned out with a special salt solution. Some of the combination is then mixed with a bit of anti-A, and some with anti-B. If agglutination takes place, a little red splotch appears at the bottom of the small tube in which the mixing took place and the rest of the liquid remains pink and no splotch appears.

Now, if the blood being examined agglutinates with anti-A only the person being tested is of blood type A. If it agglutinates with anti-B only, he is of blood type B. If it agglutinates with both anti-A and anti-B, he is of blood type AB, and if it agglutinates with neither, he is of blood type O.

Naturally, it would be helpful if anti-A and anti-B agglutinins could be located elsewhere than in blood, so that blood typing can be done without having to have on hand blood samples of known type. Actually, such materials can be isolated from many plants. These *plant agglutinins* usually agglutinate the red cells in any kind of blood but some exist which will agglutinate only A blood, or only A and O blood. There are even one or two that will hit B red cells more than they will other types. It was the American biochemist, William C. Boyd, who first discovered these choosy plant agglutinins and he named them *lectins* from the Latin word *legere*, meaning "to choose."

Generally, in typing blood it is best to test the plasma too, to see whether it contains anti-A, anti-B, both or neither (according to the kind of red cells, taken from individuals of known blood group, that it will agglutinate). This acts as a check to guard against accidents and mistakes. (Laboratory technicians are human and make mistakes, and in blood grouping, a mistake may kill a patient.) Thus, if a person's red cells seem to contain A substance and yet his plasma seems to contain anti-A, something is wrong; there is a mistake somewhere. The determination must be repeated.

The quantity (*titer*) of anti-A or anti-B in plasma varies from individual to individual. An unusually high titer of either in the donor's plasma can cause enough damage to a patient's red cells to spoil the otherwise good affects of the transfusion. Thus, occasional O donors have such high titers of anti-A, for instance, that they can't be used as donors for A patients. During World War II, the agglutinin titer of O blood was routinely taken and only those of low titer were used universally, while those of high titer were restricted for the use of O patients only·

In 1941, the practice was also instituted of neutralizing

the anti-A and anti-B in blood by adding purified A substance or B substance obtained from animal blood. The agglutinins are thus tied up and the danger of adverse reaction is cut down considerably.

Often, one need only use the plasma portion of blood in transfusion, since the red cell reserve in the spleen can carry the patient even if no new red cells are added. It is the shortage of plasma that is more immediately dangerous since that may reduce blood pressure to dangerously low levels. If plasma alone is used there are, moreover, certain advantages involved. Plasma keeps better than whole blood does. It can even be frozen and dried under vacuum (*freeze-drying*) to form a kind of "instant plasma" that can keep indefinitely and requires only sterile distilled water to reform the original liquid.

Then, too, with no red cells present there is no worry about blood types and agglutination. For that reason, plasma from different donors can be mixed without worrying about blood types. In fact, such mixing is even beneficial since small quantities of A and B substance in solution in the blood of A and B donors neutralize the anti-A and anti-B agglutinins of the mixed plasma, so that such a mixture is less likely to do damage than a single sample would.

Despite all this, it is important to remember that plasma is not always sufficient. It is not an invariable replacement for blood. For that reason, it continues to make good sense for you to know what your blood type is, just in case. (I, myself, am B.)

You inherit your blood type. There are certain structures in the original sperm cell (contributed by the father) and egg cell or ovum (contributed by the mother) called *genes*. These control the nature of various chemical mechanisms in the body cells as they develop from the fertilized ovum (that is, the cell resulting from fusion of sperm and egg). These chemical mechanisms in turn control the various detectable characteristics of the human being.

For instance, there is a gene in the sperm cell and one in the ovum which determines whether the human being that results from their union and subsequent development is to develop A substance in his red cells or B substance. Suppose, in a particular case, both sperm and ovum carried the gene that governs those chemical reactions that will result in the formation of A substance. Call it the A gene. In that case, the person that results from the fusion of that sperm and ovum will have two A genes. We can speak of him as being AA. In the same way, a person may have a double dose of B gene or of O gene (the O gene directing the formation of neither A nor B substance) and be BB or OO.

A person who is AA belongs to blood type A, naturally. One who is BB is blood type B and one who is OO is blood type O.

If an AA person marries another AA person, each parent contributes an A gene to each child that is born and all the children are AA. If a BB person marries another BB person, or an OO marries another OO, then all the children are respectively, BB or OO.

If an AA person marries a BB person (it doesn't matter which parent is which, by the way; an A gene or B gene in the sperm cell is exactly like an A gene or B gene in the egg cell and in the final fertilized ovum formed by the union of the two, it makes no difference which gene originated in which), then the AA parent contributes an A gene while the BB parent contributes a B gene. All the children inherit one A gene and one B gene. Each is an AB and is of blood type AB.

So far everything seems simple and straightforward and the inheritance of the four blood types seems to be explained. There are, however, complications.

Consider, for instance, the case of a marriage between an AA person and an OO person. One contributes an A gene, the other an O gene. All the children are AO. But here is the important thing to remember. An AO person carrying only one gene controlling the formation of A substance will form A substance just about as well as an AA person with two genes of the sort. (This is analogous to the individual with only one eye who can read as well as a person with two.)

What this means is that an AO person and an AA person both belong to blood type A. In the same way, exactly, a BO person and a BB person both belong to blood type B. If you just test the blood of an individual with plasma agglutinins there is no way of telling the difference between AO and AA. The particular gene combination of an individual is known as the *genotype*. The characteristic controlled by the genes, as it actually appears to observation, is the *phenotype*. An AO person and an AA person belong to two different genotypes, then, but to the same phenotype.

However, it is sometimes possible to distinguish an AO from an AA (or a BO from a BB) by methods other than the use of agglutinins.

Suppose, for instance that a married couple are both AO. The sperm cells produced by the husband carry only one gene for this particular characteristic. It may be an A gene. It may be an O gene. Both types are available equally and it is just a matter of chance whether a particular sperm cell has one or the other. As a matter of fact, the most probable distribution would be for half the sperm cells to carry an A gene and half an O gene. In the same way, a particular egg cell produced by the mother has an equal chance of carrying either the A gene or the O gene.

Now if, in such a marriage, a sperm happens to fertilize an ovum, one of four possible combinations can result:

(1) An A sperm can fertilize an A ovum
(2) An A sperm can fertilize an O ovum
(3) An O sperm can fertilize an A ovum
(4) An O sperm can fertilize an O ovum

Each of the four combinations is equally possible.

In case (1) the child ends up as an AA individual. In cases (2) and (3) the child ends up as an AO individual; remember it doesn't matter whether an A sperm fertilizes an O ovum or an O sperm fertilizes an A ovum; the end result is the same. In all three cases, the child of the marriage belongs to blood type A. Case (4) is, however, the interesting one. It results in an OO individual; a child of blood type O.

So you see, if two people both of blood type A, marry and have even one child of blood type O, it means that both mother and father are AO individuals. If either one of them (or both) were AA, all the children would have to be of blood type A, since in this case at least one parent would have no O gene to contribute and a person must have an O gene from each parent to end up as OO, the only combination resulting in blood type O.

The reverse, however, is not true. Suppose a married couple, both of blood type A, have any number of children, all of blood type A. That does not necessarily mean that either parent is AA. They might both be AO, but just as a matter of chance all their children resulted from fertilizations of the types shown in cases (1), (2) and (3) above. No case (4) happened to happen.

That is why, although you can't always tell a person's genotype by considering his phenotype, you can sometimes tell it if you consider not only his own phenotype but also those of his children, parents or other relatives, but only sometimes.

Several interesting things follow from all this.

Suppose an AO man marries a BO woman and has a son who is AB, a daughter who is AO, another daughter who is BO, and another son who is OO. (All these types are possible as the result of the various combinations that can take place between AO and BO.) From the standpoint of phenotype, the father and elder daughter are of blood type A; the mother and younger daughter are of blood type B; the elder son is of blood type AB and the younger son is of blood type O.

Now suppose that the younger son, the one of blood type O, needs a transfusion of blood in a hurry. Neither his mother nor his father, his brother nor either sister can offer their blood. Any one of them, no matter how dearly they loved the child, would harm him and probably kill him, if his or her blood were used. A complete stranger, a foreigner, a man from the other side of the world could be used, however, provided only that he were also of blood type O.

This despite the fact that the members of one family are of "the same blood" and that "blood is thicker than water."

Blood groups can be used to settle paternity disputes. Suppose a man of blood type B has married a woman of blood type O. Since anyone of blood type O must have the genotype OO, the mother could contribute only egg cells carrying an O gene. The B father might be BB; he also might be BO. The sperm he produces might therefore carry a B gene or an O gene.

Only two final combinations can result in children of this union. They can be either BO or OO, which represent phenotypes of B and O respectively. It follows, then, that a marriage between a blood type B and a blood type O can result in children with either a blood type B or a blood type O and in nothing else.

Suppose a child of such a marriage is tested and found

to be of blood type A. It doesn't matter whether the geno-type is AA or AO. In either case, it could not have re-sulted from the marriage. Neither father nor mother has an A gene to give it. Either the wrong baby was accidentally given to the mother at the hospital (which is unlikely, but not unheard of); or (more likely), the husband is not the real father of the child.

The reverse is not true. Suppose this same couple had a child of blood type B or O. That does not prove that the husband is the real father. Another man, also of blood type B (or even O) could have been involved. Blood tests can never tell you that a certain man is the father; they can only tell that a certain man is not the father.

Take another case. Suppose a woman of blood type B accuses a man of blood type A of being the father of her child. Well, the woman could be either BB or BO. The man could be AA or AO. The ovum could have contained either a B gene or an O gene. The sperm cell could have contained either an A gene or an O gene. The combinations that could result would be AO (blood type A), BO (blood type B), OO (blood type O) or AB (blood type AB).

The result is that the child could be any of the four types and still be the offspring of the accused man. The man could find no safety, even if innocent, in blood tests, be-cause he couldn't possibly be disqualified, if these four types were the only ones that could be identified.

Fortunately, the investigator is not at the end of his rope. As long ago as 1911, it was noticed that blood from in-dividuals of blood type A can be divided into two *sub-groups*. In most people of blood type A, the red cells react quite strongly with anti-A preparations. The cells clump together hard and come down. In a minority of cases, however, the reaction is rather weak.

People with the more common strongly-reacting A blood are said to belong to blood type A_1, the others to blood type A_2.

These sub-groups are also inherited. In the case discussed just above, if the accused man were of blood type A_1, while the child was of blood type A_2 or A_2B, his innocence is proved. There is some ground for uncertainty at this point, though. The sub-groups A_1 and A_2 are not always as easily distinguishable as are groups A and B, for instance.

It is possible, by the way, for a child to inherit the A_1

gene from one parent and the A₂ from the other. In that
case, he is A₁A₂. The A₁ gene is *dominant* in this combination
(that is, its characteristics show up, so that, analogously,
the A and B genes are each dominant over the O gene, but
neither is dominant in the AB combination), so that the
A₁A₂ child is of blood type A₁

The A, B, O, AB blood types are the important ones to
consider in ordinary blood transfusions. These types are
governed by a single family of genes. This means that a
sperm or ovum may have an A gene, a B gene or an O gene,
but not more than one. Such family of genes, only one of
which can be present in a particular sperm or ovum, are
called *alleles*.

A number of other blood group substances, however,
governed by genes that are not alleles of those controlling
A and B substances, have also been discovered. In 1927, for
instance, Landsteiner and his co-worker, P. Levine, were
deliberately injecting human red cells into the blood stream
of rabbits. The idea was to get the rabbit to manufacture
agglutinins in its blood stream which would react specifically
with the foreign and unwanted red cells being injected, causing them to clump and be put out of the way. Not enough
red cells were injected to harm the rabbit, but only enough
to develop the agglutinins. (Animals, including human beings,
have the capacity to develop substances that will neutralize
foreign molecules. Sometimes the results are good as when
immunity is developed to certain disease. Sometimes they are
bad as when an allergy is developed to a harmless substance. The subject will come up again in later chapters.)

Once the rabbit has been *immunized* to the red cells, a
sample of its blood was withdrawn and the liquid portion
separated out. The liquid portion is generally referred to
as the plasma, but in the proccess of separating it, some of
the dissolved material in the plasma is also removed and
what is left over is called *serum;* plural, *sera.* Because the
serum from the blood of immunized rabbits contains specific
agglutinins against a particular type of red cell, they are
called *anti-sera* (the Greek prefix *anti* means "against").
Scientists who spend most of their time working with sera
and anti-sera, by the way, are now called *serologists* or
immunologists.

If an anti-serum, so produced, is mixed with red cells of

the type to which the rabbit was immunized, the red cells and the agglutinins ought to combine and neutralize each other. Eventually, all the agglutinin is neutralized and what is left of the anti-serum ought to have no further effect on any blood.

Landsteiner and Levine, however, found this reasoning incorrect. Some of their anti-sera, after being completely neutralized, still had the capacity to agglutinate the blood cells of A, B, O and AB individuals. Not all blood was affected, but some of each type. Those blood specimens not agglutinated by one anti-serum could be agglutinated by a second, while some blood specimens could be agglutinated by both.

The conclusion that was arrived at was that red cells possessed blood group substances other than the usual A, B, O and AB. These were not noticed in the ordinary blood typing procedures because human blood contained no agglutinins against these new substances. For that same reason, the new substances did not affect tranfusions and didn't show up in that way. Nevertheless, they were there and when a rabbit was forced to manufacture agglutinins against them, they could be found.

Furthermore, the new group substances were not alleles of the A, B, O, AB group. A person of blood group A might or might not have a particular one of the new substances. So might a person of blood group B or of blood group O.

Landsteiner and Levine called the new substances M and N. These were governed by a pair of alleles. That is, a sperm of ovum might contain an M gene or an N gene, but not both. It might contain either of these in combination with any of the A, B, O group. If both parents contribute an M gene (or both an N gene), the child is MM (or NN) and is of blood type M (or N). If one parent contributes an M gene and the other an N gene, the child is MN and belongs to blood type MN, since as in the case of A and B neither is dominant and the blood cells of such individuals react to both anti-M and anti-N sera. (In 1947, rarer alleles of M and N, symbolized as S and s, were reported.)

The M and N blood types can be used to sharpen paternity determination. A man of blood type BM can not be the parent of a child of blood type BN, and vice versa. If husband and wife are both BM, the child cannot (or, rather, should not) be BMN or BN, while if one parent is BM and the other

BN, the child must be (or, rather, should be) of blood type BMN.

A number of other kinds of blood groups have been discovered and are being discovered. By the 1960's, at least nine sets were known and these could be combined in over a million different ways. So many are turning up that it is quite conceivable that, eventually, each person's blood will prove to be as characteristic and individual (barring identical twins) as his fingerprints. Nevertheless, with one exception, no groups other than the original A, B, O and AB are of particular importance to blood transfusion or would come to the notice of the physician in his ordinary practice.

The one exception consists of blood group substances that are under the control of still a third series of alleles. These were discovered by Landsteiner and his co-worker, the American serologist A. S. Wiener, in 1940. They were immunizing rabbits to red cells taken from a Rhesus monkey, and antisera were produced that would agglutinate certain human blood samples and not others, quite independently of whether the blood was A, B, O or AB, or of whether it was M, N or MN, either. New groups were obviously involved and these were named the *Rh* groups from the first two letters of Rhesus monkey.

Inheritance of the Rh groups is quite complicated because there are nearly a dozen different alleles controlling them. In fact, the method of naming the various alleles so as to show clearly how they might be inherited is a matter of considerable dispute. Wiener sticks to a system he first introduced and a group of British serologists have introduced a second. There are lively arguments over the matter.

To non-serologists, however, the important thing is that there is one allele, symbolized as *rh* (small letters), toward which all the other alleles are dominant. The individual never shows it unless he has a double dose, rhrh. If this happens, the person is said to be *Rh-negative*. Any person possessing only one rh gene, or none at all, having one or both his genes of that series consisting of alleles other than rh, is *Rh-positive*. In the United States, about 85 per cent of the population is Rh-positive, 15 per cent Rh-negative.

Sometimes transfusion difficulties arose when patient and donor were different in Rh, particularly if the patient had received a number of transfusions. The main interest arose, however, when it was found that Rh incompatibility could result in serious troubles for unborn children.

Such troubles arise almost invariably in cases where an Rh-negative mother has a child by an Rh-positive father. The fetus she carries is then usually Rh-positive. Now the blood of mother and fetus are often incompatible, even in the major A, B, O groups, but this is not serious in itself since the blood of mother and fetus do not intermingle. The blood vessels belonging to each break up into fine capillaries in a special organ called the *placenta* developed by the mother during pregnancy. Oxygen and food molecules can diffuse across the placental membranes from the mother's capillaries to the fetus's. Carbon dioxide and waste products diffuse back in the other direction.

Although no red cells cross the placenta in either direction, it is possible for some of the blood group substances to work loose of the red cell and diffuse across. If the blood group is incompatible with the new blood which it enters, an agglutinin may be developed against it. To what an extent this happens depends upon the particular group substance and the quantity that leaks across. For some reason, Rh-positive substance, diffusing across into the blood of an Rh-negative mother will occasionally (say, once in twenty times) produce an unusually high titer of anti-Rh-positive agglutinins.

So far, that's not bad, but the anti-Rh-positive agglutinins formed by the mother can now diffuse back into the blood of the fetus and combine with the Rh-positive red cells it finds there. Damage can be extensive, leading to miscarriage or still-birth. Even if the child is born alive, it is suffering from a condition known as *erythroblastosis fetalis,* which generally requires a complete transfusion of blood, so that the infant can quickly start fresh, and without the fatal agglutinin.

Nowadays, prospective mothers are routinely blood-typed for Rh as well as for the ordinary groups. A potential case of erythroblastosis finds the doctors ready.

Chapter 7

A Slight Change in Recipe

NOW THAT I HAVE INTRODUCED the notion of inherited variations in the chemical structure of the red cell, the subject can be pursued further. For instance, hemoglobin itself can exist in several variations and these variations can be inherited with, sometimes, serious consequences.

To begin with, hemoglobin, in the vast majority of human beings is simply hemoglobin. My hemoglobin is enough like your hemoglobin, in all probability, to prove indistinguishable to chemists. This normal and usual kind of hemoglobin is now called *hemoglobin A*.

The red cells in the blood of fetuses contains a hemoglobin, however, that is slightly different from the ordinary hemoglobin. For one thing, the two hemoglobins have different electrical properties, and this warrants some discussion.

All proteins carry electric charges at various spots on the surfaces of their large molecules. There are two types of electric charge, positive and negative, and all proteins carry some of each. All these charges of both types added together give the protein's *net charge*. The net charge is positive if there are more individual positive charges than negative. Or the net charge can be negative if the reverse is true. Or it may be zero, if there are equal numbers of each kind of charge on the molecule.

If an electric current is run through a solution of protein, those protein molecules with a net positive charge are attracted to the negative electrode, while those with a net negative charge are attracted to the positive electrode. Those with a zero charge remain motionless. The velocity with which the individual protein molecule travels depends upon its size and shape, upon the size of the net charge, and upon the pattern of individual positive and negative charges on its surface, among other things. There is enough room for variation here to make fairly certain that two different proteins will travel at different rates under the influence of an electric current.

Closely related protein molecules, which seem quite identical in most characteristics, may well have patterns of electric charges sufficiently different to produce different rates of travel. If a solution containing some of each type of protein molecule is subjected to an electric current for a period of time, one type travels more quickly than the other and the two types begin to separate, just as two groups of runners will separate as they proceed along the race course, if one group runs faster than the other.

This process of allowing closely related proteins to separate through their behavior in an electric field is called *electrophoresis*. Complicated apparatus has been devised to enable chemists to follow the course of the separation by noticing slight differences in the refraction (i.e. bending) of a light ray that passes through the solution at different points. Lately, a simplified version of the process has been achieved by allowing the proteins to travel along a piece of porous paper soaked in the solution. This is called *paper electrophoresis*.

The hemoglobin in fetal red cells, which differs electrophoretically from normal hemoglobin, is called *fetal hemoglobin* or *hemoglobin F*.

Another difference between hemoglobin F and hemoglobin A (the A, you see, stands for "adult") is that hemoglobin F has a tighter grip on oxygen. If a solution of hemoglobin A and one of hemoglobin F were mixed and exposed to oxygen, the hemoglobin F would pick up the lion's share.

This is obviously for the benefit of the fetus, which is buried inside the mother's body and must depend for its oxygen supply on molecules of oxygen diffusing from the mother's blood stream across the placental membrane into the fetus's blood stream. The mother's red cells with their hemoglobin A are one side of the membrane, while the fetus's red cells with their hemoglobin F are on the other side.

Since hemoglobin F has a stronger grip on oxygen molecules, there is less free oxygen on the fetal side than on the mother's side. Since diffusion goes from the more concentrated to the less, this situation keeps the oxygen flowing from mother to child.

Nevertheless, almost from the beginning, the fetus is manufacturing hemoglobin A in preparation for its forthcoming independent life. By the time the fetus is twenty weeks old, one-sixteenth of its hemoglobin molecules are hemoglobin A. By the time it is nine months old and emerges into the open atmosphere as a new-born baby, one-fifth of its hemoglobin molecules are hemoglobin A. Four months after birth, the hemoglobin F is almost all gone.

However useful hemoglobin F is to a fetus, it is apparently not much good to an adult. Sometimes it happens that a human being may inherit a defective gene from one of his parents (or the gene may become defective through accident during formation of sperm or ovum), which cannot perform efficiently its task of overseeing the chemical formation of hemoglobin A. This leaves the person with only one gene to do the job; remember that each person has two of each sort of gene, one inherited from the mother and one from the father. The one normal gene can almost do the work of both, but not quite. The body limps along, making too little hemoglobin A for its needs and filling in what is lacking by continuing to make hemoglobin F. (Any human being can make hemoglobin F in emergencies like this, as otherwise he would never have survived to be born.) This condition is called *thalassemia minor* and is not very serious.

However, a person may pick up a defective gene of this sort both from father and mother. Such an unfortunate individual would have no gene capable of doing full-time work on hemoglobin A manufacture. The amount of hemoglobin F in his blood cells would be anywhere up to a full 100 per cent. This is *thalassemia major* and this, generally, is fatal in early life.

Other kinds of abnormal hemoglobin molecules have been found in recent years. In 1910, James B. Herrick, examining a twenty-year-old West Indian Negro, found red cells in his blood that were of unusual shape. They curved something like the blade of a sickle and he called them sickle-cells. After that, other people, almost invariably Negroes, were also found to suffer from such a condition. By 1928, it was recognized as an inherited condition and it was found that in this disease the red cells sickled when the oygen concentration in blood was lower than normal.

In 1949, the American chemist, Linus Pauling and his co-workers showed that red cells sickled because of their content of an abnormal hemoglobin, which they called *hemoglobin S.* (The S stands for sickle-cells.) It could be picked up easily enough by electrophoresis. Hemoglobin F moves more slowly under standard electrophoretic conditions than does homoglobin A, and hemoglobin S moves more slowly still.

The chief trouble with hemoglobin S, apparently, is that it is considerably less soluble than either hemoglobin A or hemoglobin F; only one twenty-fifth as soluble as hemoglobin A, in fact. Hemoglobin is packed pretty tightly into the red cells and there is just enough fluid in the cells to keep the hemoglobin moving freely about, if it is the fairly soluble hemoglobin A or F. If some of the hemoglobin is hemoglobin S, however, this, being less soluble, forms small solid crystals. These crystals bulge out the red cell membrane and distort it into the sickle shape. Now oxyhemoglobin S is just as soluble as oxyhemoglobin A, so it is only when the oxygen concentration in the blood falls and the oxyhemoglobin S is converted to hemoglobin S that sickling takes place.

If the red cells stayed in this sickle shape, there would be trouble. Not only are they less efficient at picking up oxygen, but the distorted membrane is unusually fragile with the result that such cells break up more rapidly than normal cells would. An anemia results.

Fortunately for individuals with only one gene for hemoglobin S (and this includes most of the Negroes whose red cells can be made to sickle in the test-tube) sickle-cell formation does not take place to any important extent in their blood under ordinary living conditions. They can carry on a normal life and with a normal life-expectancy.

It is the occasional child who inherits a hemoglobin S gene from each parent who is really in trouble. Such a child, with two genes for hemoglobin S and none for hemoglobin A, produces no hemoglobin A at all, only hemoglobin S and possibly some hemoglobin F. In these children, the red cells sickle extensively even under ordinary conditions of life, and anemia, called *sickle-cell anemia,* or *sicklemia,* develops. Death usually comes early in life.

Now, why does hemoglobin S seem to occur in Negroes only? How did it start? It is possible, sometimes, not to transmit a gene as it occurs to begin with. In the process of forming the sperm cell or egg cell, part of the chemical structure of the gene may be accidentally changed. Its structure is very complicated and in repeated reproductions of that structure, mistakes and imperfections may creep in. The changed gene may be one which then produces hemoglobin S rather than hemoglobin A. Such a change in a gene and the appearance of a brand-new characteristic in a child not present in the parents is called a *mutation*.

Now a particular mutation does not happen very often. It is possible that it happened once to some African Negro many generations ago and never happened again, and that it appears today only in those who can trace at least some of their genes back to that original one, and consequently only in Negroes.

Tropical Africa is certainly the focus of the S gene, and hemoglobin S occurs more frequently there than anywhere else in the world. American Negroes inherit the S gene from their African ancesters, but because they have intermixed with other Americans to a considerable extent, the hemoglobin S gene has been "diluted" and there is a smaller percentage of it. But still, one American Negro out of eleven has one hemoglobin S gene so that sickling can be detected in his blood. This is called *sickle-cell trait*. It is harmless and not to be confused with sickle-cell anemia. One American Negro out of five hundred is born with two hemoglobin S genes and suffers from sickle-cell anemia.

Now if you were to start with a population that carried a certain number of genes for hemoglobin S, you might expect that gradually, over the years, that gene would die out. Every once in a while, two such genes would come together and the unlucky person who was at the receiving end would probably die before he could have children to whom to pass them on. There would go two genes. This slow but steady trickle toward destruction ought eventually to deplete the gene. So it might under ordinary circumstances. Perhaps a hemoglobin S gene was formed by mutation elsewhere than in Africa, but died out after having started. Perhaps it got started by accident only in Africa and then found an environment that was just right to keep it going. If so, what might that environment be?

One clue to the answer of the riddle has been recently uncovered. In the regions where hemoglobin S gene is common, malaria is also common. It seems that people with one hemoglobin S gene are less susceptible to malaria. Perhaps the malaria parasite, which infests the red cells of people who have contracted the disease, finds the hemoglobin S in the red cells of people with sickle-cell trait not quite to its finicky taste. For that reason, that part of the population carrying one hemoglobin S gene will tend to live longer, on the average, and be stronger while alive, and have time to produce more children, than do those without.

The advantage of being resistant to malaria with a single dose of hemoglobin S gene tends to increase the occurrence of that gene. The disadvantage of dying with a double dose of it tends to decrease the occurrence. The two tendencies balance and an equilibrium results. The equilibrium is high where malaria is particularly virulent and lower where it is not.

Perhaps if modern medicine brought new standards of insect control and hygiene to the affected regions of Africa, the incidence of malaria and with it that of hemoglobin S would decline. We can't be certain, though, since it is possible that this matter of malaria is not the whole story.

Since hemoglobin S was discovered, a whole series of abnormal hemoglobins have shown up and it's hard to say whether there's an end in sight. Probably not. They are identified usually by their different electrophoretic properties and are then given letters. So far, we have (in addition to A, F and S) hemoglobins C, D, E, G, H, I, J, K, L and M.

Hemoglobins G, H, I, J, K, L and M have only been detected in one or two families and practically nothing is known about them except that they exist. They, as well as hemoglobins C, D, E and S are governed by genes that are alleles of the normal hemoglobin gene. If you have an abnormal hemoglobin gene, it takes the place of a normal gene. This is not true of hemoglobin F, which is not an allele of hemoglobin A. No matter what the state of your ordinary hemoglobin genes, you have at least one intact hemoglobin F gene, or you could not have survived to be born.

Of the more common abnormal hemoglobins, hemoglobin D has been picked up among the people in northern India, the incidence being about 1 per cent.

Hemoglobin C is found most frequently among African

Negroes as is hemoglobin S. The incidence of hemoglobin C is more restricted though, occurring only in West Africa, rather than throughout tropical Africa as does hemoglobin S. The highest incidence is reported in the northern regions of the new state of Ghana (formerly the Gold Coast). There, about 28 per cent of the hemoglobin genes are hemoglobin C.

As in the case of hemoglobin S, single doses of hemoglobin C (or of any of the abnormal hemoglobins) are not serious. A single dose of hemoglobin C, in fact, is possibly also protective against malaria and there are signs that the gene originated out of a fairly recent mutation and is still spreading outward through the malarial regions. It is possible, incidentally, but rare, that a child might inherit two genes for different abnormal hemoglobins; a hemoglobin S gene from one parent and a hemoglobin C gene from the other. This is bad and usually means death at a young age.

Hemoglobin E occurs most frequently in southeast Asia. In Thailand, 13 per cent of the hemoglobin genes in the population are reported to be for hemoglobin E. In Jakarta, the capital of Indonesia, 6 per cent of the hemoglobin genes are for hemoglobin E. There is some speculation whether single doses of hemoglobin D and E may allow a person to make use of iron more efficiently and therefore be able to get along on less iron.

If all this is true, it looks as though the picture may be this. Abnormal hemoglobins are developing all the time because of random changes (mutations) in the hemoglobin genes. Almost always, the abnormal hemoglobin is less efficient than the normal one and if there are no balancing virtues (as there usually are not), they die out after a while. Perhaps the very rare abnormal hemoglobins that have been detected are in just this case; mutations that have occurred quite recently and that may die out after several generations.

If, on the other hand, a single dose of the abnormal hemoglobin gene serves to help humans get along under borderline conditions of nutrition or disease, as do those genes for hemoglobin C, D, E and S, they survive at whatever equilibrium value represents a balance of their virtues and defects, supposing enough time has elapsed for a balance to be reached. If that is so, you would expect abnormal hemoglobins to occur most often in regions of low standards of living and so they do. (Of course, if ever an abnormal hemoglobin were developed which, in double dose, was superior to hemoglobin A, it would take over and hemoglobin A would die out.)

Naturally, scientists have been curious to know in exactly what way the various hemoglobins differed among themselves. They behave differently electrophoretically and so there must be some chemical difference, but finding it wasn't easy.

The ordinary methods of testing proteins showed hemoglobin A and hemoglobin S to be just about the same in chemical makeup. No differences could be detected. However, each molecule contains about 8,000 atoms. If only a few of those atoms were misplaced or out of arrangement, that might account for the difference, and yet the few misplaced atoms would be hard to notice among all the thousands of correctly placed ones.

Nevertheless, the problem now seems to have been solved.

In the first place, the atoms in protein molecules are not arranged any old way, higgledy-piggledy. They clump together into small groups, forming compounds known as *amino acids,* but these amino acids (alas) are arranged in no easily predictable order. There are nineteen different kinds of amino acids that each occur in just about all proteins, and an additional score or so that occur in certain particular proteins but not in the general run. Hemoglobin has no unusual amino acids in its molecule; only the nineteen general ones.

The hemoglobin molecule is made up of about six hundred amino acid units. There are as many as seventy-five of one type and only a single specimen of another, while the rest fall between. Since they are not arranged in any repeating order, the problem of working out which amino acid goes where might seem to be an insoluble one. The number of possible arrangements of the amino acids in a hemoglobin molecule is more than 10^{619}, which is the number 1 followed by 619 zeroes. This is a tidy quantity and not to be sneezed at.

Of course, each hemoglobin molecule is made of identical halves, so that it is really only necessary to work out the arrangement of three hundred amino acids of a "semi-hemoglobin" molecule, but this is still too much to handle. It is necessary for the molecule to be broken up into smaller pieces.

Vernon M. Ingram, at Cambridge University, did just that by treating the hemoglobin molecule with a digestive enzyme called *trypsin*. Trypsin will cause a chain of amino acids to break at whatever points particular amino acids named *lysine* and *arginine* occur. The result is that under treatment, the "semi-hemoglobin" falls apart into twenty-eight fragments.

These individual fragments are short chains of amino acids which are called *peptides*. Some might contain only two or three amino acids, some might contain a dozen or more, depending on the exact spacing of lysine and arginine groups in the original chain. All twenty-eight peptides are, of course, mixed together and have to be separated.

To do this, a drop of the mixture is placed on porous paper (called *filter paper* because its original use in chemistry laboratories was to filter out fine solid particles from liquids), which is then wet with an appropriate fluid. Two electrodes are attached and an electric current is sent through the paper. The peptides, just as proteins would, travel toward either the positive or the negative electrodes at varying speeds, according to the number and pattern of electrical charges carried by each peptide. This is the paper electrophoresis I mentioned earlier.

The process divides the peptides into several groups, strung along the paper. The resulting "spots" are not visible to the naked eye, but can be made visible in different ways. The paper can be treated with chemicals, which will react with the peptides to form colored compounds; or ultra-violet light is used so that ordinarily invisible compounds may absorb the light and appear black or, possibly, may fluoresce and shine. Each spot still contains several peptides of similar electrical properties, so each group must be separated further. This is done by a process called *chromatography*, which is worth explaining in some detail.

Chromatography began in 1906 with a Russian botanist named Michael Tswett. He was interested in trying to separate the various colored pigments that could be soaked out of plant leaves. These pigments were so similar in chemical composition that ordinary methods for separating chemical compounds didn't work too well. Tswett tried a completely new technique.

He took the solution of the pigment mixture and poured it through a long column of powdered limestone. The pigments stuck to the surface of the tiny particles, but the liquid in which they were dissolved passed through unaffected. The colored solution with which Tswett had started came out of the column colorless, and at the top of the column was a colored band of pigment stuck to the limestone.

Tswett next ran another liquid, called petroleum ether, down the column. Slowly, this washed out the pigment. Each different kind of pigment in the mixture was washed out at a different rate. Those that clung rather loosely (or were particularly soluble in petroleum ether) washed down rather rapidly; those that clung more tightly (or were not particularly soluble in petroleum ether) washed down more slowly. In time, the original mixture of pigments was separated into a number of colored bands each made up of one particular compound. These bands could be washed completely out of the column, one after the other, and studied separately.

Tswett called this technique *chromatography* from Greek words meaning "color writing" because the answer to the composition of the mixture was written in colored bands along the length of the tube. The procedure works, of course, for colorless compounds, too.

For many years nothing came of this because Tswett's first report was in a rather obscure German botanical journal and his later, fuller reports were in Russian. Furthermore, he was a Russian and only a botanist and the German biochemists (who ruled the roost in those days) paid no attention to him. However, in 1931, a German biochemist, Richard Willstätter, came across the technique and started using it. It quickly grew in importance, thereafter.

Other powders besides limestone were used. Aluminum oxide, starch, and most recently, *ion-exchange resins* became popular. The resins are amber-colored brittle substances with large molecules containing numerous atom groupings which, through chemical reactions, could hold on to certain types of molecules under some conditions and let them go again under others. Resins of different composition will have different properties and be suitable for different jobs. Some will even desalt water. Sea water can be put in at one end of a tube and drinkable water will emerge at the other.

A still further advance was made in 1944 when a group of British biochemists at Cambridge University showed that a separation of compounds in a mixture could be carried out on filter paper. Instead of letting a solvent trickle down a column of powder, they let it creep down (or up) a sheet of filter paper. As the solvent passes the spot where a bit of the unknown mixture has been placed and allowed to dry, the solvent drags the components of the mixture with it; each component being dragged at some characteristic speed. The one spot of mixture is converted into a number of spots of individual components. This solvent-creeping trick is called *paper chromatography* and it is, today, perhaps the most important technique in the biochemist's bag of tricks. Almost any research, of whatever sort, ends up in the separation of a mixture or the purification of a single substance by paper chromatography.

To get back to Dr. Ingram now, and the peptide mixture he obtained from hemoglobin.

We left him with a number of spots on paper, obtained by paper electrophoresis, each containing several peptides. He next applied paper chromatography. He allowed a solvent to creep across the line of spots and to separate each spot into a number of sub-spots, so to speak.

When he was finished, he had twenty-eight different spots spread across the length and width of the filter paper. He numbered each of these spots and then proceeded to try the very same trick from the beginning on hemoglobin S molecules, instead of hemoglobin A. From it, too, he developed twenty-eight different spots.

In a way, he had fingerprinted each molecule and now he had only to compare fingerprints. It turned out that hemoglobin A and hemoglobin S showed a spot pattern that was identical, except for a single detail. The spot which in the hemoglobin A pattern Ingram had numbered 4 was shifted distinctly to the left in the hemoglobin S pattern.

So Dr. Ingram repeated the experiment a number of times for both hemoglobin A and hemoglobin S, cut out spot 4 each time, and dissolved the material out of the paper until he had enough to work with. This part was tedious, of course, but very necessary.

Spot 4 turned out to be a peptide made up of a string of nine amino acids. The peptide was broken apart by treatment with hydrochloric acid into still smaller strings and eventually into single amino acid units. These were separated and analyzed and after considerable painstaking work, the arrangement of amino acids in the hemoglobin A spot 4 was shown to be:

histidine—valine—leucine—leucine—threonine—proline—glutamic acid-glutamic acid-lysine
(all these being names of various amino acids), while the arrangement in the hemoglobin S spot 4 was:
histidine—valine—leucine—leucine—threonine—proline—valine—glutamic acid-lysine

If you compare the two lists, you will see that they differ in only one respect. Where the hemoglobin A has a glutamic acid, the hemoglobin S has a valine. As far as we know now, that is the only difference between the two molecules; a difference of two amino acids (one in each of the identical halves of hemoglobin) out of six hundred.

One of Dr. Ingram's colleagues, John Hunt, tried the same thing with hemoglobin C and once again spot 4 was different. In fact, it had split in two. In hemoglobin C, there turned out to be a lysine in place of the glutamic acid of hemoglobin A (or the valine of hemoglobin S). Since the enzyme, trypsin, which had been used to split the original molecule did its work at lysine groups, the spot 4 peptide in hemoglobin C was split into two peptides, one of seven amino acids and one of only two.

It all makes sense electrophoretically. The glutamic acid of hemoglobin A carries a negative charge. The valine of hemoglobin S has no charge at all. The lysine of hemoglobin C carries a positive charge. The charge pattern is different in each and they should behave differently in an electric field and they do.

Of course, like all spectacular solutions in science, additional problems are immediately raised. Why should such a slight change in recipe for the putting together of the hemoglobin molecule make such a difference in solubility, in antimalarial resistance and so on? Then, too, how do the genes dictate the exact recipe for preparing the molecule? How do they manage to supervise the stringing together of six hundred amino acids just so? And what can go wrong with a gene that makes it get one and only one amino acid displaced?

There'll be an answer someday, I'm sure, but it hasn't come yet.

Chapter 8

Expelling the Undesirables

ONCE THE OXYGEN IS SAFELY INSIDE THE CELL, *thanks to hemoglobin* and the blood stream, it combines (through a series of a great many different chemical reactions, each controlled by an appropriate enzyme) with the atoms of molecules that have been obtained in one way or another from the food we eat. There are innumerable kinds of molecules in food, but in the main they are all made up of only four different kinds of atoms: carbon, hydrogen, oxygen and nitrogen. These four, together, make up about 99 per cent of the atoms in the food we eat.

The hydrogen atoms in *organic compounds* (that is, carbon-containing compounds of the type found in living tissue and, consequently, in food) will combine easily with oxygen under body conditions, forming water. (The water molecule is made up of two hydrogen atoms and one oxygen atom.) The carbon atoms in organic compounds will combine with oxygen as easily to form carbon dioxide. (The carbon dioxide molecule is made up of one carbon atom and two oxygen atoms.)

In the process, energy is liberated. A mixture of organic compound and oxygen contains more energy than the mixture of carbon dioxide and water produced by their interaction. The energy left over in going from the first mixture to the second makes its appearance in the form of the heat. When we burn coal, oil, natural gas, wood, paper and so on, the carbon and hydrogen in those substances combine with oxygen and we thankfully use the energy which makes its appearance. If the reaction is sufficiently rapid, light will appear in addition to heat.

The combinations that go on in the body are much slower and more carefully controlled than those that go on in a bonfire. No light is produced in the body and even heat production is kept to a minimum; in the main, the energy is stored in the form of chemical compounds that are high in energy content. These in turn power the muscles, run the nerves, supply energy for making complicated molecules such as protein and so on.

(The oxygen already present in the food molecules won't convert more than a small fraction of the carbon and hydrogen to carbon dioxide and water. The body needs a large additional supply from the atmosphere to do the job. Nevertheless, the food oxygen does its part and also ends up in the water and carbon dioxide molecules eventually.)

Granted, now, that cell chemistry has achieved all this. The cells have stored or used what they could of the energy produced and gotten rid of what was left over as heat. (The body is only perhaps 40 per cent efficient, which sounds disappointingly low, but is actually higher than the efficiency of manmade machines such as steam engines, and internal combustion engines, which run on the energy of burning carbon and hydrogen atoms.) With all this done, the body must get rid of the chemical compounds left over; the "ash," so to speak, the water and carbon dioxide.

The water is no problem at all. (Since the sum total of chemical reactions in living tissue are referred to as *metabolic reactions,* the water produced by such reactions is called *water of metabolism,* to distinguish it from the water we drink and which is introduced into our body as water from the beginning.) The human body has a million uses for water and, in general, we are troubled by a shortage rather than an excess of it.

The water of metabolism, plus the actual water contained in food (even a "dry" food such as bread is actually one-third water, as you would quickly realize if you tried to eat really dry bread) supplies us with only half the water we need. If we restricted ourselves to food only, we would be suffering agonies of thirst by the second day. It is for that reason that in addition to our food, we drink a quart or two of water daily (either as water itself or as some highly watery liquid such as milk, fruit juice or beer).

The need for constantly replenishing our water supply arises from the fact that water is unavoidably removed from the body in a variety of ways. The expired breath carries some off (you can see the water vapor in the breath when it condenses into fog on a cold day). Some is lost with the feces (quite a bit, in fact, under conditions of diarrhea, and it is the loss of water that makes diarrhea in infants, who have a smaller water supply to begin with, dangerous). Some is lost constantly as perspiration even on cool days. Finally, you lose a quantity as urine.

The body can hang on to some of the water if it has to. If your water intake doesn't keep pace with your needs, the urine is made more concentrated; less water is used by the body in carrying off the waste-products. The ordinary daily volume of urine is about 1,300 milliliters. It can be cut down, in case of necessity, to as little as 500 milliliters. But that is about the limit. Even if you were dying of thirst, the body would still be losing some of the water you so desperately needed. In fact, that is exactly the reason why you would be dying of thirst.

The urine is also the safety valve which protects us from drowning in our own fluid on those rare occasions when we do have more water than we need. If, for instance, an enthusiasm for beer, let us say, brings one to the point where enough is downed to supply the body with water in unwanted quantity, the body can get rid of it simply and quickly through the kidneys. A dilute and copious urine results, as beer-drinkers well know.

Some animals, particularly those that live in the desert, have evolved methods of conserving water that are superior to our own. The water in the food they eat and the water of metabolism they produce, in addition, is then enough to replace the dribbles they lose. Such animals can be featured in "Believe it or Not" columns as animals that "never drink."

Carbon dioxide is considerably more of a problem than water of metabolism. The body has uses for carbon dioxide, but not for all that is produced. The body must get rid of the excess, as it is produced, or die. The cells solve the immediate problem for themselves by allowing the carbon dioxide to diffuse out into the blood stream. The blood thus serves as air-line and exhaust simultaneously, which sounds inefficient but works fine.

Once the blood reaches the lungs, it rids itself of its excess carbon dioxide, which, like oxygen, is a gas. As the blood moves along the alveoli of the lungs, carbon dioxide molecules diffuse into the air-pockets in the lung at the very time that oxygen molecules are diffusing into the blood. In each case, the diffusion is from the side of the greater concentration to that of the lesser. As a result, although the inspired air is 20 per cent oxygen and 0·03 per cent carbon dioxide, expired air is 15 per cent oxygen and 5 per cent carbon dioxide. (In each case, the rest of the air is nitrogen.)

The question then arises as to just how carbon dioxide is carried in the blood. In one respect, the problem is not as serious as is that of carrying oxygen. Oxygen is only slightly soluble in water so that hemoglobin has to be depended on for oxygen transport. Carbon dioxide, on the other hand, is quite soluble in water. To be exact, 100 milliliters of water at body temperature will dissolve only 2·5 milliliters of oxygen, but fully 53 milliliters of carbon dioxide. This would virtually solve the problem of carbon dioxide transport, if all that were in question were simply getting rid of carbon dioxide and nothing more.

Actually, though, the chemical properties of carbon dioxide introduce additional complications and the body makes use of those complications to retain a sizable quantity of this particular waste product in order to allow it to serve certain vital functions. To get at this will require a detour.

Carbon dioxide molecules do not merely dissolve in water; they react with water molecules to form *carbonic acid*. We can represent this by a chemical equation using C as the symbol of carbon, O for oxygen and H for hydrogen:

$$CO_2 + H_2O \rightleftharpoons H_2CO_3$$

carbon dioxide   water   carbonic acid

Ordinarily, this reaction proceeds very slowly, but in the

blood stream there is something to help it along. The carbon dioxide that enters the plasma from the cells can penetrate the red cell membrane easily so that some of the carbon dioxide molecules inevitably find themselves within the red cell. There is an enzyme within the red cell which has the specific job of hastening the combination of carbon dioxide and water. (Enzymes in general have the job of hastening reactions that would proceed without them, but much more slowly.) This particular enzyme is called *carbonic anhydrase* and is unusual in that its molecule contains at least one atom of the metal, *zinc*. (There are other zinc-containing enzymes also, but this one alone is enough to explain why zinc is an essential metal for human life. It is needed only in traces, of course, and any reasonable diet has enough of it for our needs.) In the presence of carbonic anhydrase, carbonic acid is quickly formed and drifts back out across the red cell membrane into the plasma.

There is also a tendency for carbonic acid to break up again into carbon dioxide and water. That is why the equation written earlier has an arrow in each direction. Carbonic anhydrase accelerates the breakup as well as the formation of the carbonic acid. The result of this action-in-both-directions is that a point is reached where carbonic acid is being formed just as fast as it is breaking down and that is the *equilibrium point*. In the blood, therefore, there is both carbon dioxide and carbonic acid.

In the lungs, only the carbon dioxide diffuses across the alveolar membranes into the air spaces. Carbonic acid cannot do so because it is not a gas. However, as carbon dioxide escapes from the blood, the delicate equilibrium between itself and carbonic acid is upset. Some of the carbonic acid breaks up into water and carbon dioxide to maintain the equilibrium, and the carbon dioxide so formed may also escape into the lungs. Carbonic acid does not, therefore, by any means interfere with the body's scheme of carbon dioxide removal.

Carbonic acid can break up in another way, too. It is, as its name states, an *acid*. An acid is any substance whose molecule has a tendency to lose a portion of one or more of its hydrogen atoms. This portion of the hydrogen atom is missing one electron and is called a *hydrogen ion*. The portion left over, containing the extra electron that had belonged to the missing hydrogen, is the *bicarbonate ion*. This breakup also moves both ways, and also reaches an equilibrium. The chemical equation for the breakup is:

$$H_2CO_3 \rightleftharpoons HCO_3^- + H^+$$

The resulting ions are electrically charged (which is what makes them ions). The bicarbonate ion carries a negative charge and the hydrogen ion a positive charge, and this is indicated by the presence of a small minus sign and plus sign respectively to the upper right of the formula of the ions.

So now it turns out that when carbon dioxide is discharged into the blood, it shows up as three different substances: carbon dioxide itself, carbonic acid and bicarbonate ion. All three are in a state of balance. Add a bit of any one of the three and the added bit changes partly into the other two. Withdraw a bit of any one of the three and the other two change partly to replace most of what is missing. Thus, when carbon dioxide escapes into the lungs, and carbonic acid breaks up to form more carbon dioxide, some bicarbonate ion adds on hydrogen ion to form more carbonic acid. The body doesn't do all this purposely; it is merely following the cold and objective laws of chemical equilibrium. Still, the result is that any change is, in this way, spread over a larger area, so to speak, and minimized. This is a most useful thing for living tissue, which is a delicate and fragile thing that cannot withstand sudden change of any kind.

Don't misinterpret that last statement. We, as organisms, can withstand sudden change. We can step from an overheated house out into a below-zero winter's day without trouble, but that is only because when we do so the internal temperature of our body does not change. A great part of the chemical activity of the body is involved in just the business of preventing outer changes from disturbing the calm level of the inner environment of the tissues.

As an example, take this balance between carbonic acid and bicarbonate ion which has just been under discussion. It represents one of the most important chemical devices by which the body manages to cushion our delicate cells against change, and is the reason why the body can never afford to get rid of all its carbon dioxide but must keep some of this "waste substance" to maintain life.

Let's begin with water again. The water molecule is made up of two hydrogen atoms and an oxygen atom, and has a very slight tendency to break up spontaneously in such a way as to lose a hydrogen ion (as described in connection with carbonic acid, above). What is left over (an oxygen atom plus a hydrogen atom plus the electron left behind by the departing hydrogen ion) is called the *hydroxyl ion*.

This *ionization* of water is another reaction that goes both ways, so that an equilibrium is reached. At the equilibrium, in pure water, most of the water molecules at any one instant of time remain intact. Only one out of some sixty billion water molecules is ionized. For every sixty billion molecules of water, then, there is one hydrogen ion and one hydroxyl ion. The fact that there are equal quantities of each ion, make water a *neutral substance*.

These two types of ions maintain an inverse balance (i.e. in the manner of a see-saw). If anything is done to increase the hydrogen ion concentration, the hydroxyl ion concentration correspondingly drops. The solution is then said to be acid; the greater the preponderance of hydrogen ion, the more acid. On the other hand, if anything is done to decrease the hydrogen ion concentration, the hydroxyl ion concentration correspondingly rises. The solution is then said to be basic, or alkaline (the two words are synonymous); the greater the deficiency of hydrogen ion, the more basic. (As long as water is present, the concentration of neither ion ever reaches zero.)

The hydrogen ion is one of the most active chemical substances there is. Almost any chemical reaction will go faster or slower, depending on the concentration of hydrogen ion in its vicinity. The body, which depends on thousands of reactions, each going just so, must see to it that the hydrogen ion concentration in its tissues is at a desirable level.

As far as the blood is concerned, this desirable concentration is a little on the basic side of neutrality. There are only one quarter as many hydrogen ions in blood as there would be if it were quite neutral—say, one hydrogen ion for every two hundred forty billion molecules of water.

This small quantity must be protected. If the concentration of hydrogen ion rises by 35 per cent or falls by 25 per cent, the body chemistry is sufficiently disorganized to bring about death. And yet in the course of body chemistry, compounds that are themselves acidic or basic in nature are continually being produced or consumed. These may be dumped into the blood stream to some extent or be withdrawn from the blood stream. In either case they will act to shift the hydrogen ion concentration in one direction or the other, and this shift must be kept to a minimum.

(Chemists represent the hydrogen ion concentration by a figure they call the pH. The pH at the neutral point is 7·0. Lower figures imply an acid solution; the lower, the more acid. Higher figures imply a basic solution; the higher, the more basic. What's more, the variation is logarithmic. That is, a solution with a pH of 6·0 has ten times the hydrogen ion concentration of one of 7·0. A pH of 5·0 implies a hydrogen ion concentration ten times higher still. Similarly, a solution with a pH of 8·0 has a hydrogen ion concentration only one-tenth that of one of 7·0. On such a scale, the pH of the blood is 7·4 and must not be allowed to fall below 7·32 or rise above 7·46.

One of the most important shields against a fatal shift in pH is the carbon dioxide/carbonic acid/bicarbonate ion combination in the blood.

Suppose for instance, that in the course of the body's chemical workings, a quantity of acid substance is released into the blood stream. This acts as a new source of hydrogen ion so that the hydrogen ion concentration in blood begins to climb and the pH to fall.

But as soon as these extra hydrogen ions make their appearance some will combine with the bicarbonate ion present, forming carbonic acid which, in turn, breaks down to form carbon dioxide which can be expelled through the lungs. In this way, excess hydrogen ions are used up and the pH shift is minimized.

Suppose, on the other hand, that a quantity of basic substance is released into the blood; a substance, that is, which has a strong tendency to combine with hydrogen ions and withdraw them from solution, lowering the hydrogen ion level below the danger point.

Before this can happen, however, the carbon dioxide system takes over again, this time in reverse. The carbonic acid gives up hydrogen ions to replace what is being lost and is, in this way, converted to bicarbonate ion. To keep the carbonic acid from being consumed in this fashion, some carbon dioxide which would ordinarily be allowed to escape into the lungs is held back and allowed to combine with water to form new carbonic acid.

So the carbon dioxide system protects the blood against

harmful changes in pH in either direction. The bicarbonate ion acts like an empty sponge which sops up hydrogen ions when there are too many of them. The carbonic acid acts like a full sponge which squeezes itself to supply some hydrogen ions when there are too few of them. Between the two, the pH is kept constant.

The carbonic acid/bicarbonate ion system is an example of what chemists call a *buffer*.

The blood contains other buffers, but the carbonic acid/bicarbonate ion system is the most useful because it is under more delicate control than the others. It alone, of all the buffers, is in equilibrium with a gas that can be eliminated more quickly (by increasing the breathing rate) or less quickly (by slowing the breathing rate).

Actually, it is the carbon dioxide in the blood that controls the rate of breathing, and not the state of the oxygen supply. Ordinarily, this is fine since, generally, if you have too much carbon dioxide in the blood, you are also short of oxygen. If you breathe rapidly in order to get rid of the first, you also automatically get a good supply of the second. And the reverse is true.

Since the rate of breathing can regulate the pH of the blood, you can shift the latter by playing about with the former. For instance, you can deliberately force yourself to breathe quickly and deeply for a period of time. This flushes carbon dioxide out of your body, causing carbonic acid to break down too quickly in an attempt to replace the carbon dioxide, which in turn causes the bicarbonate ion to tie up too much hydrogen ion in an attempt to replace the carbonic acid. The net result is a lowering of hydrogen ion concentration and an increase of the blood pH to bring about a *respiratory alkalosis*. You are then "oxygen drunk," and feel giddy. If you kept it up, you would lose consciousness, but before that point arrives you are usually in no position to keep it up. You "let go" and breathe very slowly (or even stop breathing) until the carbon dioxide catches up.

You can also hold your breath for a couple of minutes, allowing carbon dioxide to accumulate, which in turn forces the carbonic acid to accumulate, which in turn releases more hydrogen ion into the blood. The net result is a raising of hydrogen ion concentration and a decrease of the blood pH to bring about a *respiratory acidosis*. Again, you are forced to let go before unconsciousness comes about (usually) and must, in this case, pant for a period of time to flush out excess carbon dioxide.

Carbon dioxide is not transported by the blood by means of ordinary solution alone. In fact, hemoglobin, which has as its primary function the transport of oxygen, will also serve to carry carbon dioxide.

Carbon dioxide can combine with one of the amino acids (the one called lysine) that occur in protein molecules. The combination is called a *carbamino compound*. It so happens that hemoglobin is not only the most plentiful protein in blood, but it also contains more lysine than does any other blood protein. The result is that about one-fifth of all the carbon dioxide in venous blood is in the form of *carbaminohemoglobin*.

Furthermore, hemoglobin does more than simply act as transport. It connives actively to force carbon dioxide out of the body and into the lungs.

Let's take a closer look at what happens as the blood in the pulmonary artery—bluish, deprived of oxygen, loaded with carbon dioxide in solution, some combined with water to form carbonic acid and bicarbonate ion, and some combined with hemoglobin—approaches the alveolar capillaries.

The first thing that happens is that oxygen drifts across the alveolar membrane into the blood and changes the hemoglobin to oxyhemoglobin.

Two things follow: first, oxyhemoglobin does not form carbamino compounds as readily as hemoglobin does. About two-thirds of the carbamino groups in the hemoglobin break down at once as a consequence and carbon dioxide is set free.

Secondly, oxyhemoglobin is a stronger acid than hemoglobin is and produces more hydrogen ions. (All proteins are acids to a certain extent; they all have a tendency to ionize and produce hydrogen ions.) The blood as it absorbs oxygen from the lungs, suddenly finds itself with an increased supply of hydrogen ions. The buffer systems go into action at once. Bicarbonate ion combines with the excess hydrogen ion to form carbonic acid which, in turn, breaks down to carbon dioxide.

Thus, in two different ways, the change of hemoglobin to oxyhemoglobin encourages the formation of carbon dioxide in the blood so that carbon dioxide is given a push, so to speak, as it goes drifting across the alveolar membrane into the air within the lungs. It is then breathed out and the body is done with it.

Carbon dioxide and water of metabolism are the waste products formed from the carbon and hydrogen atoms in foodstuffs. That leaves the nitrogen atoms, which occur, for the most part, in proteins, where they are found to the extent of about one atom out of every twelve.

It would be nice if those nitrogen atoms could be converted into a gaseous waste to be disposed of through the lungs in the fashion of carbon dioxide. Perhaps the first thought that might arise in anyone approaching the subject without preconceived notions is: since carbon and hydrogen are combined with oxygen and then excreted, why can't nitrogen be combined with oxygen too, and handled in the same way. After all, the various nitrogen oxides are gases.

Unfortunately, there is a catch here. When hydrogen and carbon combine with water, they move into a state of lower energy and the energy left over is available for the use of the body. Nitrogen, on the other hand, in combining with oxygen, moves into a state of higher energy, so that to form the nitrogen oxides energy must be added to the system. This is a lucky thing for us, since it keeps the nitrogen and oxygen in the air from going up in one big explosion. Instead, the energy situation doesn't allow them to combine even when a forest fire is raging or a blast furnace is pouring intense heat into the air. It takes the energy of a lightning bolt to combine nitrogen and oxygen and then only in its immediate vicinity, and the body can't afford to use lightning-bolt levels of energy just to get rid of wastes.

Why not, however, liberate the nitrogen as nitrogen gas. There are no energy objections to this, yet the fact remains that no organism above the level of the bacteria (microorganisms as a group are much more versatile, chemically, than are multi-cellular organisms) has developed the chemical machinery to do that.

The next best thing is to turn the nitrogen into *ammonia* (which has a molecule consisting of one nitrogen atom and three hydrogen atoms). This represents an energy waste because less energy is produced by converting protein to water, carbon dioxide and ammonia, than by converting it to water, carbon dioxide and nitrogen. However, the waste is less than 2 per cent, and the little bit of extra energy gained by going all the way to nitrogen has apparently never made it worth while for organisms to develop the necessary machinery.

Ammonia is a gas, but it is extremely soluble in water. One hundred milliliters of cold water will dissolve 110,000 milliliters of ammonia gas. As fast as ammonia is formed, it will dissolve in the body water.

But this raises a problem instantly. Ammonia is a very poisonous substance. If there were as little as a thousandth of a milligram of ammonia in a liter of blood, that would be enough to kill.

Ammonia must therefore be removed from the body as fast as it is formed. The only way that can be done is for the organism to be surrounded, continuously, by a vast quantity of water into which the ammonia can be dumped; so vast a quantity of water that the ammonia is instantly diluted below the danger point and kept there. This means that only creatures dwelling in oceans or other bodies of water can afford the luxury of getting rid of nitrogen in the form of ammonia. In case you are wondering whether, as a result of all the ammonia dumped during billions of years, the oceans might not eventually fill up to danger point and whether, in fact, they should not have done so many ages ago, stop worrying. The ammonia is used by the one-celled plants that crowd the ocean surface and is rebuilt by them into the protein on which the sea-animals feed and which they then reconvert into ammonia. This is part of the *nitrogen cycle*, and as a result of this cycle the oceans remain comfortably ammonia-free.

When life began invading dry land, it had to adapt itself to an environment in which water was scarce. It took its pinch of ocean with it in the form of a blood stream, but it was only a pinch. Pouring ammonia into the water supply within a single organism would raise the concentration of ammonia to the poisonous level almost at once, and there is no way of pouring water out of the organism fast enough to keep the ammonia level down, unless the organism can arrange some method of renewing its water supply equally quickly. On dry land that quick removal simply cannot be arranged, or at least never has been.

Nitrogen therefore had to be excreted in a form that was less toxic than ammonia or the dry land was doomed to remain unconquered by animal life. Fortunately, the solution was found. Two molecules of ammonia could combine with a molecule of carbon dioxide to form a compound known as *urea.* (Its molecule contains one carbon atom, one oxygen atom, two nitrogen atoms and four hydrogen atoms.)

Urea is a solid substance, but it is over twice as soluble as table salt so that the body has no difficulty in getting it into the blood stream. Furthermore, it is quite safe in comparison with ammonia. The liter of blood that dared not contain even a thousandth of a milligram of ammonia can (and does) contain 40 milligrams of urea without ill effect.

The result is that when tadpoles, for instance, change to frogs, they switch from the ammonia system of getting rid of nitrogen wastes, to the urea system. It is the part of the change we don't see. The loss of the tail and the growth of the legs are obvious. The switch from gills to lungs is only slightly less obvious. The change in chemistry, however, though it is not in the least obvious, is more fundamental than either of the other switches and more essential.

Urea contains more energy than ammonia does, so that animals that make use of urea as the nitrogen waste give up some of the energy that might otherwise be made available to them. However, the advantages they gain are worth much more than the trifle of energy they lose.

Certain insects, birds and reptiles spend the first several days or weeks of their lives inside eggs placed on dry land. Within those eggs, the water supply is not only limited but it cannot be renewed even by such a restricted device as drinking. So the method of removing nitrogen must be changed again. If urea were formed in the eggs, the concentration of that substance would reach a poisonous level (even urea becomes poisonous if enough of it accumulates) before hatching. Nitrogen is therefore excreted in the form of *uric acid,* a compound somewhat more complicated than urea and containing fragments of four ammonia molecules and three carbon dioxide molecules. Uric acid is quite insoluble, so it doesn't enter water in any quantity to speak of. Instead, it is stored away in odd corners within the egg where it won't bother the developing organism. Uric acid involves a slight energy loss even when compared with urea, but here again the advantages gained make the energy loss worth while.

Mammals, including man, the young of which develop for weeks or months within the mother's body, retain the more primitive urea system. The urea formed by the fetus diffuses across the placental membranes into the mother's blood stream so that the water supply available to them is quite ample for their needs, and mammals have never, as a consequence, had to develop the uric acid system.

Plants, which lack the circulating fluid animals have, also have the problem of disposing of nitrogen. Some solve the problem by forming complex nitrogen-containing compounds called *alkaloids,* which they then store in bark, roots, seeds or leaves. These generally have powerful effects on animal chemistry when taken internally and many of them have proven great boons or deadly poisons, depending on the dose.

If the cells discharged urea into the blood stream and that were all there was to it, the quantity of urea in the blood would quickly reach a poisonous level. However, at one point in its travels about the body, the blood passes through two bean-shaped organs located at about the small of the back (one on each side of the backbone), called the *kidneys.*

The kidneys, like the lungs, are spongy masses of tissue in which the blood stream finds itself separated from the outside world only by microscopically thin membranes. Where the lungs are subdivided into tiny vacuoles along the boundaries of which the blood passes, the kidneys have tiny *tubules.* As the blood passes along the tubules, a quantity of water, together with all the small molecules held in solution, including urea, diffuse through the tubule membrane into the outer world.

As the solution travels down the tubule duct, however, some of the water and virtually all the useful substances that the body needs are reabsorbed; that is, drawn back into the blood stream. Waste products, such as urea, plus enough water to keep it in solution is not reabsorbed. This solution of waste substance is the *urine.* Microscopic quantities of urine pass down each of the billions of kidney tubules into long tubes (one leading from each kidney) called *ureters.* The ureters lead the urine into a single *bladder,* where it accumulates and from which it is periodically discharged. (Some of the wastes in urine are pigments; that is, have color; and it is this that gives urine its amber appearance.)

With the body cells continually forming urea and the kidney continually removing it, the amount of urea in the blood is kept at a low and fairly constant level. If the kidneys, through infection or other disease, falter in their constant filtering action, the urea concentration begins to build up in the blood. This condition is called *uremia* and is eventually fatal. Such is the importance of kidney action that the kidney has its own means of keeping the blood flow steady. If, for any reason, the flow slows, the kidney liberates an enzyme called *renin*. This acts to change one of the proteins in blood to a compound called *hypertensin*, or *angiotonin*. This constricts various blood vessels, raising blood pressure and speeding the flow.

Earlier in the chapter, I mentioned how the water content in the body could be adjusted to some extent by eliminating a concentrated urine during times of water shortage and a dilute one during times of water over-supply. The kidney controls this by adjusting the amount of water that is reabsorbed from the tubules. Much is reabsorbed if the body is short of water; little is reabsorbed if it has an over-supply.

This kidney action is in turn controlled by a chemical named *vasopressin*, formed in small quantities by the *pituitary* gland, a small organ situated at the base of the brain. There are occasionally individuals in whom the pituitary fails in this respect. Vasopressin is not formed and the control over kidney action is lost.

When this happens, little or no water can be reabsorbed in the kidney tubules, so that the afflicted person must eliminate large quantities of dilute urine, up to 5 quarts a day or even more. This disease is known as *diabetes insipidus*. The term "diabetes" comes from a Greek word meaning "a siphon" and in this case it certainly seems that the patient (who is, naturally, always thirsty and must be constantly drinking) is merely siphoning water through his body. The "insipidus" means "tasteless" and distinguishes this disease from other types of diabetes by indicating that the urine, in this case, is so dilute as to be practically water. Patients with diabetes insipidus can be helped, and the disease kept under control (though not cured) by injections of vasopressin obtained from the pituitaries of domestic animals.

Vasopressin is an example of a *hormone;* that is of a chemical which is formed by a special organ called a *gland,* is discharged into the blood stream and controls some part of the body chemistry. Many hormones (but not all) are proteins with, usually, rather small molecules. Vasopressin, for instance, has a molecule of eight amino acids (as compared with six hundred amino acids in the hemoglobin molecule). In 1953, a group of biochemists at Cornell University Medical School in New York, under the leadership of Vincent du Vigneaud, synthesized this hormone, the first protein hormone ever to be manufactured by anything but an animal's gland.

This synthesis was the final proof of the exact structure of the vasopressin molecule and could be an important step forward in our understanding of how hormones work. So far, scientists are not clear as to the exact chemical mechanism by which any hormone accomplishes its task. In view of the tremendous importance of hormones to the body, the disorders caused when the body forms too much or too little of a particular hormone, and the help various hormones are in treating certain disorders; the understanding of hormones is high on the biochemists lists of "musts." For his work in this and other branches of biochemistry, Vincent du Vigneaud received the 1955 Nobel Prize for Chemistry.

Chapter 9

The Salt of the Earth

So FAR, we have considered two points at which the blood comes into contact with the outside world (separated from it by membranes, of course): at the lungs and at the kidneys. The lung serves as both entrance and exit for gases; oxygen entering the blood; carbon dioxide and water vapor leaving it. The kidneys serve as an exit only for liquid substances; water, that is, carrying urea and other wastes in solution.

That leaves one remaining point of contact between blood and the outside world; the *alimentary canal*. The alimentary canal is a continuous tube extending from the lips to the anus. It is open to the outside world at both ends so that material within the tract is not yet within the body, really. (Analogously, an object inside the hole of a doughnut is not inside the doughnut; and water passing through a pipe is not inside the metal of the pipe itself.)

When we eat, food enters the alimentary canal, passing through mouth, throat and *esophagus* (or *gullet*) in quick succession and entering the *stomach*, where it may remain for hours. Solid food, as such, cannot be handled by the body. Only substances in gaseous or liquid form (including solid material in solution, of course) can diffuse across a membrane and enter the body. For that reason, we chew our food and mix it with *saliva* before swallowing. In the stomach the food is further mixed with a quantity of *gastric juice*, a liquid secreted by small glands in the lining of the stomach (as saliva

115

is secreted by somewhat larger glands in the cheeks and jaws). Both saliva and gastric juice contain enzymes which speed the breakdown of some of the larger molecules in food to smaller pieces. The net result is that by the time the food is ready to leave the stomach and enter the *small intestine* (where the main business of the alimentary canal is transacted), it is a thick liquid.

(Some animals, notably the cow, which subsist on coarse food such as grass, spend a great deal of time in chewing. Carnivorous animals, like cats and dogs, which eat meat—and meat is, on the whole, more easily liquefied in the stomach than is plant food—lack saliva and bolt pieces of food whole. Birds, which also bolt food whole, usually possess crops or gizzards, sometimes filled with small pieces of gravel which the bird had deliberately swallowed and which act as internal jaws to give the food a preliminary breakup. In every case, though, the food leaves the stomach in essentially liquid form.)

The small intestine is the most important part of the alimentary tract. It is a long tube, twenty feet in length or more, which only fits into a human being by being coiled and coiled again, practically filling the abdominal cavity in the process.

At the very beginning of the small intestine (the *duodenum*), more fluid pours into the food from two large glands, the *liver* and the *pancreas*. The liver fluid, or *bile,* contains no enzymes but helps break up the fat content of the food into small, easily handled droplets. The *pancreatic juice* contains a number of enzymes, in contrast.

As the food travels further along the intestine, still more fluid, containing additional enzymes, enters from small glands in the intestinal wall itself. This is the *intestinal juice.* All these fluids succeed in watering down the food into a thin liquid, while the various enzymes succeed in breaking up most of the large molecules in food into molecules small enough to diffuse across a membrane, and that is the object of the whole process, which we call *digestion.*

The interior of a twenty-foot tube such as the small intestine offers a reasonably large surface through which molecules might be taken into the body, but this surface is increased still further by the fact that the entire interior of the tube is covered with tiny thin-walled projections called *villi.* (The effect is that of a Turkish towel, which can absorb more water than can a dish-towel of the same size because the Turkish towel has all those loops acting as further absorbers.) Inside each villus is a capillary, so that once again, we have the situation we had in lungs and kidney. On one side of a thin membrane is a capillary, on the other side, the outside world.

Water can pass from the intestine across the membrane into the blood stream (and vice versa). Along with the water, there will travel small molecules of various substances obtained from the food after the breakdown of the large molecules by digestion. The passage of material from the intestinal canal into the blood stream is *absorption*.

By the time food passes out of the small intestine and into the shorter but wider-bored *large intestine,* it consists largely of water (from all the fluid added at one point or another in the canal) and substances that have resisted digestion and remain in the form of large molecules that will not cross a membrane. These indigestible substances consist largely of fibrous materials from plants and some from animals. While not contributing to the workings of the body, since they are never absorbed, they are useful in adding bulk to the diet; in giving the intestine something to hold on to, so to speak, while it is absorbing what it can.

In the large intestine, water is reabsorbed. The water has served its purpose and there is no sense in wasting it. So the intestinal contents become less watery as they progress along the large intestine and by the time what is left of the food reaches the *rectum* at the end of the alimentary canal, it is once more in a solid or semi-solid state and is ready to be eliminated altogether, as *feces.*

When something goes wrong with the water reabsorption in the large intestine, so that the feces are eliminated in semi-liquid or liquid form, the condition is known as *diarrhea.* This results in an abnormal loss of body water together with the abnormal loss of certain substances that are dissolved in the water and cannot help but accompany body water wherever it is forced to go. It is this loss of water and dissolved substances that makes diarrhea so debilitating, and in the case of infants that have a much smaller reserve of these substances in the first place, the condition is quite serious and may on occasion, be fatal.

The feces contain quantities of bacteria (up to between one-quarter and one-half its weight), which have lived on the food passing through the intestines and which have multiplied wildly in the warmth and safety of what is to them an ideal home, flowing with milk and honey. The ordinary bacteria of our intestines, however, are not pathogenic (i.e. not disease-producing) and do us no harm except for depriving us of some of the food which they utilize and which would otherwise go to us. (Antibiotics are added to the feed of domestic animals in order to increase their rate of growth and this may work by slowing the rate of bacterial growth and reserving a larger fraction of the feed to the animal and less to the bacteria.)

However, intestinal bacteria, in return for the fraction of our food to which they help themselves, manufacture a number of vitamins for their own use which we are incapable of manufacturing for ourselves (as in the case of vitamin B_{12} which I mentioned in an earlier chapter). They manufacture the vitamins in quantities greater than they need and we absorb the excess feeding on their leavings as they feed on ours. This mutually helpful association between two types of organisms is called *symbiosis*.

The symbiotic arrangement is even more important to cattle than to us. Cattle feed largely on grass and other rough vegetation and this consists mainly of cellulose which is indigestible to all many-celled animals, including the cattle themselves. If cattle relied on their own digestive apparatus and nothing more, they would quickly starve to death. They (and other grass-eating animals) have, however, a complicated alimentary canal (in the case of cattle, including four separate stomachs), in which food is stored an unusually long time. The bacteria of the alimentary track can break down cellulose into usable fragments and have time to do so. (Our bacteria could probably do the same, but our alimentary canal is shorter and they lack the time.) The bacteria make use of some of the fragments and the rest are absorbed by the animal. The fact that cattle can convert grass into milk and meat is entirely thanks to the bacteria, which thus not only allow cattle to thrive, but do mankind a great service.

(On the other hand, the same principle can do us great harm. Termites live on wood, which is largely cellulose and this they cannot digest any more than we can. However, within the termite intestines live certain protozoa in efficient symbiosis. The protozoa can and do digest cellulose, and feed both themselves and the termite on the products. So while the termites gather the raw material and the protozoa process it, our houses crumble.)

But what of the material that has been absorbed into the body during the passage of food through the small intestine. This material can be divided into two classes: (1) substances that can be absorbed directly into the body (usually in the small intestine, but also in the stomach and even in the mouth) without undergoing any change from their condition in the original food; (2) substances that must be changed (i.e. digested) before being absorbed.

The first class includes water, of course, but water has been discussed in detail already. It also includes *minerals*. The minerals are so called because they occur in the body pretty much in the same form in which they are found in the non-living mineral world. They can also be considered *inorganic* substances, because a living organism is not required for their manufacture.

(In distinction to this, there are a number of substances, called *organic,* which in the days before modern chemistry, could be made only as a result of the workings of a living organism and were found in the mineral world only as the remains of organisms that had once been living. Nowadays, organic substances can be synthesized in the laboratory, along with thousands of similar substances that are not found in nature at all, either in the mineral world or in living organisms.

(Since the substances originally considered organic possess molecules that contain one or more carbon atoms, chemists have agreed to extend the notion by calling all carbon-containing substances organic, whether they can be formed by living organisms or not, or whether they are found in the mineral world or not. Similarly, any substance with molecules that do not contain carbon atoms is inorganic even when, like water, it is an absolutely essential part of the living organism.

(This is an example of something often overlooked. There are no classifications in nature. All classifications are man-made. To begin with, a particular classification may follow some seemingly logical dividing line and be named accordingly. However, as knowledge increases, classifications are shifted or modified to suit the convenience of scientists. If names then become illogical, that is too bad. The point is that classifications represent convenience with a capital C and not truth with a capital T.)

The minerals or inorganic constituents of food exist in the form of ions. These are, as I explained earlier in the book, atoms or groups of atoms containing an excess or deficiency of one or more electrons. Those that contain a deficiency of electrons possess a positive charge and include, chiefly, the *sodium ion*, the *potassium ion*, the *calcium ion* and the *magnesium ion*. Each of these is made up of a single atom. The sodium and potassium ions are missing one electron each, so that each has a single positive charge. The calcium and magnesium ions are missing two electrons each and each has a double positive charge.

The chief negatively charged ions are the *chloride ion*, which consists of a chlorine atom plus an excess electron, and the bicarbonate ion, which I talked about in the previous chapter and which is organic and not mineral. In addition there are the *phosphate ions*, which are made up of a phosphorus atom, three oxygen atoms and either two hydrogen atoms plus one excess electron, or only one hydrogen atom and two excess electrons, and the *sulfate ion*, made up of a sulfur atom and four oxygen atoms plus two excess electrons. In addition, there are simple organic compounds which carry either a negative or positive charge, more often the former, and proteins, which carry both positive and negative charges with, usually, more of the negative under body conditions.

All these ions, plus others present in trace quantities which we can ignore, are absorbed from food, or formed from it, and can be found in the blood.

The total content of the smaller ions in blood (that is, ions made up of at most half a dozen atoms) is about 10 grams per liter. Of these, the most common positive ion is the sodium ion, and the most common negative ion is the chloride ion. Common table salt is made up of these two ions only and is properly named *sodium chloride* in consequence. It is surprising, then, that blood tastes salty.

(It is important to remember that ions have properties that are quite different from the atoms from which they are formed by electron shifts. Sometimes, people will be surprised that a necessary substance like salt is made up of "sodium," a poisonous metal, and "chlorine," a poisonous gas. But, you see, salt isn't made up of these. It is made up of sodium ion and chloride ion, which are mild and gentle substances, not poisonous in ordinary amounts, and necessary to the body.)

The blood acts as a reservoir of the various ions on which the cells can draw at need, or into which they can pour their excess. As always, a delicate balance within the blood must be obtained, not too much and not too little. The bicarbonate ion balance is maintained by varying the rate of breathing, as described in the previous chapter. The other ions are kept in balance by the kidney. The ions diffuse through the tubule membrane just as water does and then they are reabsorbed as water is. If there is a shortage of a particular ion, more of it is reabsorbed and vice versa.

The kidney is more efficient at retaining some ions than others. For instance, if the supply of sodium ion runs short, the kidney can clamp down and allow the loss of no more than 10 milligrams per day. In the case of potassium ion, however, the situation is worse. Even if no potassium ion at all were entering the body, the kidneys would still allow a minimum of 240 milligrams to escape each day.

Nevertheless, despite this and despite the fact that the human body needs more potassium than sodium, there is still a greater danger of sodium deficiency than of potassium deficiency. The reason for this lies in the fact that plant life in general is richer in potassium and poorer in sodium than is animal life. The major portion of the diet of most human beings is of vegetable origin, so that they get the potassium they need but not the sodium.

For that reason, it is customary to add table salt to food to "bring out the flavor." Actually, of course, it does improve the taste and the tendency is to add more than we really need. Adding salt is, however, more than a question of taste alone. It is a vital necessity. And when Jesus wished to praise His listeners during the Sermon on the Mount (Matthew 5: 13) He used, as high compliment, the phrase, "Ye are the salt of the earth."

The need for salt is even more extreme in those animals which are strictly herbivorous and eat only plant food. Such animals search out "salt licks," which are natural accumulations of salt, and will visit them over great distances and at great hazard, with all the determination with which they seek out water.

Whenever water is lost to the body by any route, a certain number of ions must accompany it. These are the ions which I referred to earlier in the chapter as the substances lost along with water during diarrhea. They are also present in tears and in perspiration, both of which taste salty in consequence.

Loss through perspiration can be serious. Hard physical labor under conditions of heat, as in mines, in furnace-rooms or just in the hot summer sun, where there is copious perspiration loss, means loss of sodium ion as well as water. The water is easily replaced, since water loss induces thirst and, providing water is available, the perspiring man will drink without urging. However, the fresh water that he drinks, contains no sodium ion so that this is not replaced. To prevent weakness and heat prostration, salt tablets should be taken with the water and sometimes a dispenser of these tablets is placed near the water fountain.

Of course, if the body has an excess of sodium ion this must be carried off through the kidneys. For every milligram of sodium ion removed, a certain quantity of water is necessary to transport it and is used, even though the body may be short of water. That is why people suffering agonies of thirst in drifting lifeboats actually deprive themselves of water if they try, in desperation, to drink sea-water, and would live longer if they drank nothing. It is for this reason, also, that salty foods, as is well known, induce a feeling of thirst. It is the body's safeguard against the inevitable loss of water that is coming.

Recent studies have shown that certain birds and reptiles which spend their lives largely at sea but which are descended from land-living ancestors can drink sea-water and flourish. To do this, they must get rid of the excess sodium ion, since their body tissues are no saltier than ours. Fortunately for themselves, they are equipped with small "salt glands" situated at the base of their nose which excretes liquid that is very concentrated in salt. Essentially, what they do is drink salt-water, de-salt it by means of these glands, and retain the fresh water that is left. A pity we're not equally equipped.

Now why are the minerals so important? They are not used by the body for energy formation and they do not form a major part of the structure of the soft tissues. Still, there is one tissue that is not soft—bone.

Bone is made up chiefly of calcium ions and phosphate ions in the form of tiny crystals. These are slowly deposited onto the surface of growing bone, or bone that is being repaired after a break, from the supply in the blood. The end result is that in the adult body about 85 per cent of the phosphate ion and well over 99 per cent of the calcium ion is present in the bones and teeth.

But this is far from all. Ions have their uses in the soft tissues, also. For one thing, they are unevenly distributed. Any piece of matter large enough to be visible under the microscope must contain either no charged particles, or just about equal numbers of positively and negatively charged particles. In either case, there is no net charge; the piece of matter is *electrically neutral*. This holds for living tissue, too, but this rule of electroneutrality doesn't say which particular positive or negative ions must be present to form the balance.

For instance, the liquid within cells (*intracellular fluid*) is rich in potassium ions (positive) and phosphate ions (negative); while the liquid outside cells (*extracellular fluid,* including blood) is rich in sodium ions (positive) and chloride ions (negative).

This means that if we take a nerve fiber, for instance, and concentrate for the moment only on the positive ions, there is present on the cell-side of a narrow membrane a lot of potassium ion and little sodium ion, while on the extracellular-fluid-side of the same narrow membrane there is a lot of sodium ion and little potassium ion. The proportion is roughly 40 to 1 in favor of potassium within the cell and 7 to 1 in favor of sodium outside it.

This is unusual because the membrane is permeable to both sodium and potassium ions and one would think the two ought to be present in equal concentration on either side. And, in fact, if the nerve cell is killed, the two ions do indeed equalize in concentration. While the cell is alive, however, it keeps the situation unbalanced and must expend energy to do so. It is as though you kept one ball well up the side of one hill slope and another well up the side of the other hill slope. As long as you expend energy to hold them there, the situation will remain thus. Relax your hold for an instant, though, and both balls roll down to the valley between the hills.

Why should the fiber work so hard to maintain the unbalance? Well, as long as the unbalance (involving electrically charged particles, remember) exists, the membrane itself is in a state of electrical unbalance. That is, one side of the membrane has an excess of positive charge and the other side an excess of negative charge. The membrane is *polarized*. When the nerve is stimulated, some chemical change takes place within it which temporarily interrupts the ionic unbalance. Potassium ion rushes out of the cell and sodium ion rushes into the cell (both balls, in other words, roll down to the valley). The end of the nerve is *depolarized*. At once the nerve sets to work to re-establish the original unbalance, and it succeeds, but by that time, the depolarization has set off the depolarization of a further neighboring stretch of nerve.

In this way, a wave of depolarization progresses along the nerve. And with it travels what we call the *nerve impulse*, which is somehow interpreted by the brain as sight, sound, pressure, pain or any of a variety of types of information about the outside world.

The question as to the exact manner in which the body manages to maintain unequal concentrations of ions across a membrane, particularly the nerve membrane, and what happens to cause momentary depolarization is still largely in the realm of speculation.

The point to be made now is that not only are inorganic ions involved in bone formation, bone growth and bone repair, which is obvious, but they are also involved in various electrical phenomena in the body, notably in nerve action, which is a lot less obvious. To perform their tasks properly, the various ions must be in particular proportion to one another. If the proportion falls outside certain narrow limits, nerve and muscle cannot respond properly to the demands of the environment. At one extreme, muscles go into a spasm of contraction (so-called *tetany*); at the other they become loose and flaccid.

How does the body maintain the delicately balanced levels of ions in the blood and tissues?

Well, at the end of the previous chapter I mentioned a hormone called vasopressin, produced by an organ called the pituitary gland, which governed the water level, in the body by controlling the rate of reabsorption of water in the kidney tubules. This is an example of a general system. The body produces many hormones, each of which seems to control one or more facets of the body's chemical balance and some of them are involved in the control of the ion balance.

But let's go back a little and ask: what is a gland?

A gland is any organ in the body that manufactures a fluid. The various organs that manufacture the digestive fluids mentioned earlier in the chapter are glands. And yet they are not glands in the same sense that the pituitary gland is a gland.

Certain glands deliver their fluid through tubes called *ducts* to some point on the outside of the body. The sweat glands do so. So do milk-secreting glands in the breasts of the lactating female (these glands being modified sweat glands, by the way). The digestive glands fall into this group since they possess ducts and deliver their fluids into the alimentary canal which is really outside the body (as the hole in the doughnut, remember, is outside the doughnut).

However, there is another set of glands—to which group the pituitary belongs—that produce fluids that are kept within the body. Such glands do not have ducts; the fluids produced diffuse through cell membranes directly into the blood stream and are circulated by the blood to all parts of the body. These are the *ductless glands* or *endocrine glands*. It is the fluid of these ductless glands that contains the hormone controls of the body.

(The testicles, which are the sperm-producing organs in males, and the ovaries, which are the egg-producing organs in females, also produce hormones. They are ductless glands as well as cell-producers. It is for this reason that "gland" has become synonymous with "genital organ" among some sections of the public. This is a wrong use of the word, brought on by feelings of delicacy that are unnecessary, since there are respectable names for all parts of the human body.)

Some hormones, like vasopressin, are proteins of small molecular weight. The smallness is necessary since hormones must pass through membranes in going from gland to blood stream, and a large protein could not manage this. Some of these hormones, in fact, amount to little more than modifications of individual amino acids.

A second class of hormones are *steroids*. These are substances whose molecules contain 17 carbon atoms arranged in 4 rings according to a set pattern. Attached to various points in the ring are anything up to 10 carbon atoms and 5 oxygen atoms. Minor variations in the details of the structure make hundreds of different steroids possible and some of them, in the form of hormones, have exceedingly powerful effects on the body.

Two of the ductless glands in the body are small lumps of tissue above each kidney. They are the *adrenal* glands (from Latin words meaning "at the kidney") or *suprarenal* glands ("above the kidney"). Each adrenal gland is actually double. The central region, the *adrenal medulla,* does not concern us at the moment.

The outer portion of the gland is the *adrenal cortex* (cortex being a Latin word for "bark" and is used here because the outer portion surrounds the inner as the bark of the tree surrounds the trunk proper). The adrenal cortex produces a whole series of steroid hormones for which the shortest general name is *corticoids*.

Every once in a while, someone is unlucky enough to find his adrenal cortex not producing the quantity of corticoids that are needed. This is called *Addison's disease* (not after anyone who has suffered from it, but after the doctor who first described it). One of the things that happens in the course of this disease is a tendency for abnormal loss of sodium ion. Sodium ion passes through the kidney but is then not properly reabsorbed. (This situation is similar to that of water in diabetes insipidus.)

The abnormal loss of sodium ion can be checked by injecting small quantities of certain corticoids into the body. Not any corticoid will do, but only one of those that are particularly concerned with ion balance; one of the *mineralocorticoids*. The most effective mineralocorticoid known now is *aldosterone,* and this is probably the chemical which, in tiny traces, is chiefly concerned with the body mechanism for maintaining mineral balance.

But is this just pushing the problem one stage further back? If we blame mineral balance on the adrenals, why can't we ask what keeps the adrenal glands working properly? How do they know just how much corticoid to produce to keep things in proper balance? Too much corticoid secretion or too little will throw things out of balance. (Addison's disease proves that).

This brings us back to the pituitary gland. This, like the adrenal gland, is double. The back half (the *posterior lobe*) secretes several hormones, including vasopressin, but it is the front half (the *anterior lobe*) that is of prime importance. The anterior lobe of the pituitary is practically the "master gland" of the body, since it produces a number of protein hormones whose main function is to control other glands.

For instance, one hormone it produces is *adrenocortico-tropic hormone* (which means, in Latin, the "hormone causing growth of the adrenal cortex"). However, biochemists grow bored with long names, too, even though it may not not always seem so to an outsider and they call this hormone ACTH. When ACTH is secreted into the blood stream it is carried everywhere and, eventually, passes through the adrenals. At the adrenals, ACTH stimulates the production of corticoids.

The corticoids, once produced and poured into the blood stream, are in turn carried to the pituitary. If the level of corticoid in the blood were lower than normal, this would stimulate the formation of additional ACTH (which would increase the corticoid production and restore the proper level). If the level of corticoid in the blood were higher than normal, however, this would inhibit (i.e. cut down) the formation of ACTH, so that the corticoid production would decrease and again the proper level would be restored.

This interaction between pituitary and adrenal glands (the pituitary-adrenal axis, it is sometimes called) is an example of a *feedback mechanism*. A feedback mechanism, whether in a living organism or in a mechanical device, enables something to govern its behavior by gathering information as to the results of its immediately preceding behavior. When you reach for a pencil, for instance, you watch your arm and are constantly adjusting your muscular movements by noting whether your hand is overshooting or undershooting the mark. This is an example of feedback. You do this quite unconsciously and perhaps don't even believe you are doing it, but if you watch a baby try to reach for something you will see the amount of labor it takes to learn the trick. Or watch a victim of cerebral palsy and see what happens if one is physically unable to learn the trick. Or, best of all, look at a pencil, note its position, close your eyes and reach for it quickly without looking and see how often you miss.

The feedback mechanism does not involve adrenal and pituitary glands only. The actual level of sodium ion and other ions in the blood has its effect. So do other hormones. The pH and a dozen environmental factors have their effect. It is necessary to remember that the body is not a system of simple isolated push-button devices, but one interlocking complex which can't be pushed at any one place without having the effect show up in two dozen other places.

It is this which makes hormone treatment such a tricky thing. It can save lives and do good, but physicians must watch constantly for undesirable side effects or after effects.

This leaves another question. How do hormones do it?

How does a hormone go about exerting its effect? Why does a tiny quantity of aldosterone keep the kidney tubule reabsorbing sodium ion, while a very similar steroid may have no effect at all? Or for that matter how does vasopressin control water reabsorption? Or how does ACTH stimulate corticoid production and how do corticoids stimulate or inhibit ACTH production?

This is one of the problems to which biochemists still don't know the answer. There is no general agreement on how even a single one of the hormones in the body actually does its work. But there are theories and I'll get to some of them a little later on in the book.

Chapter 10

Sugar and the Islands

Now WE ARE LEFT with the organic compounds in food; those which cannot be absorbed through the intestinal walls unless they are first broken down into smaller molecules through the activity of the digestive enzymes. It is these organic compounds, that, for one thing, supply the fuel for the body; it is they that contain the carbon and hydrogen atoms which combine with oxygen and which liberate energy while doing so.

The organic compounds of food can be divided into three main classes: (1) carbohydrates, (2) proteins and (3) lipids. This division was invented before chemists knew much about the actual structure of the molecules in food, and was based more on their behavior in water than anything else.

Carbohydrates are easily dissolved in water, or if not, can be made soluble by treatment with acid. Lipids are quite insoluble in water and can be made soluble only by prolonged heating with alkali. Both are more soluble in hot water than in cold. Proteins are often soluble in cold water but become extremely insoluble in hot.

Simple chemical analysis also shows differences. Carbohydrate molecules are made up of carbon, hydrogen and oxygen atoms in the approximate proportion of 10:20:10. Lipid molecules are also made up of carbon, hydrogen and oxygen atoms, but here the approximate proportion is 10:20:1; much less oxygen, you see. Proteins also contain carbon, hydrogen and oxygen, but in addition contain nitrogen and, usually, sulfur.

Nowadays the structural differences can be pin-pointed much more exactly and satisfactorily, but this is not a book on chemistry particularly and the two paragraphs above, give us enough for our present needs.

And to begin with, we'll consider carbohydrates.

The most common carbohydrate in our food is *starch*. This is a white, easily-powdered solid that is tasteless and insoluble in cold water. It occurs as the main organic constituent of many plant foods, such as potato, rice, corn, wheat, yams, carrots, bananas and so on. It does not occur in animal foods except in very minor quantities.

Starch varies in physical nature, as in the size of the grains, for instance, from plant to plant and even in chemical nature to a small extent. All types of starch, however, are alike in the following respects. First, they are all made up of large molecules containing thousands and even millions of atoms. Secondly, their molecules are made up of six-carbon units, hooked together rather loosely, sometimes in straight chains and sometimes in branched chains.

Starch that is heated in water, with a little acid thrown in to speed things up, will break up little by little at the points of juncture of the six-carbon units until, in the long run, only individual units are left. This process is called *hydrolysis* from Latin words meaning "loosen by water." The individual unit, all of which, in the starch molecule, are identical, is *glucose*.

Enzymes in the digestive fluids encourage this hydrolysis, but do so in two steps. There is an enzyme in saliva called *salivary amylase* and one in the pancreatic juice called *pancreatic amylase,* which are much alike. Both bring about the stepwise breakdown of starch into two-unit groups. ("Amylase" comes from the Latin *amylum* meaning "starch.") This two-unit group, glucose-glucose, so to speak, is called *maltose*.

By the time food is well into the small intestine, the original starch is all or almost all in the form of maltose and there the first stage of starch digestion comes to an end. But even the maltose molecule is too large (or perhaps otherwise unsuitable) for diffusion through the intestinal membranes. The second stage of digestion now follows, when still another enzyme, one in the intestinal juice this time, takes over the job.

This new enzyme, *maltase,* brings about a hydrolysis of the maltose molecule into its two glucose halves. (The "ase" suffix, by the way, is the hallmark of enzyme names, except for those few enzymes which were discovered and named before the "ase" suffix was agreed upon.)

Then, finally, once the glucose is formed, absorption can take place; starch has been broken down sufficiently to enter the body.

As starch is broken down into smaller chains of glucose units, either by acid or by enzyme action, two changes take place in its properties: it becomes more soluble and it becomes sweet to the taste. Maltose and glucose are both quite soluble and both are moderately sweet. The word "glucose" derives in fact from a Greek word meaning "sweet." Small carbohydrate molecules with these properties of solubility and sweetness are usually lumped under the heading of *sugars.*

Another giant molecule carbohydrate occurring in plants, and therefore in our diets, is cellulose, which I mentioned in the previous chapter as being indigestible. Oddly enough, it, like starch, is composed of long strings of glucose units. In cellulose, however, the glucose units are joined (the proper chemical term for it is *condensed*) in a slightly different way from that in starch. There are no enzymes in the animal body that can handle the type of glucose condensation in cellulose; and furthermore this cellulose type of condensation results in a stronger and tougher molecule than that of starch could possibly be.

It is an example of the versatility of life that the same fundamental building block condensed in one way will serve as a food store for the plant, as well as for the animals that appropriate it, while condensed another way will serve as a sturdy and adequate support for trees that may be hundreds of feet tall and supply equally sturdy beams for our houses.

There are two sugars that, as such, also make up an important part of the human diet. One is ordinary table sugar for which the chemical name is *sucrose,* though most people, other than professional chemists, are content to call it "sugar." Sucrose is made up of two six-carbon units as maltose is, but in sucrose the two units are not alike. One is glucose, to be sure, but the other is *fructose,* another six-carbon sugar, quite similar to glucose, but with two of the hydrogen atoms it contains located differently. (The properties of a compound depend not only on the kinds of atoms present in the molecule and on the number of each, but also on the exact arrangement of the atoms. Something of the sort shows up in our number system and it can therefore be used as an illustration; there is no mistaking the difference between \$120 and \$210.)

Sucrose cannot be absorbed through the intestines any more than maltose can, so it, too, must be broken down. There is an enzyme, *sucrase*, in the intestinal juice which takes care of that, hydrolyzing sucrose to the individual units, glucose and fructose, both of which can be absorbed easily.

(Incidentally, the existence of small changes in atom arrangements within molecules do not necessarily require delicate chemical testing for detection. Even small changes can shout their existence. Fructose, for instance, though differing very slightly from glucose is fully twice as sweet, so you can tell by taste which is which. Furthermore, powdered fructose will absorb water from the air and become a hard cake, whereas powdered glucose will remain relatively dry and powdery. So you can tell by sight, too, which is which.)

The second sugar in the diet occurs only in milk and is called *lactose* (from a Latin word for "milk") or, sometimes, *milk sugar*. It, like sucrose, is a two-unit sugar and one of the units is glucose. The second unit, however, is still another six-carbon sugar, again differing only slightly in actual atom arrangement from both glucose and fructose. This sugar is *galactose* (from a Greek word for "milk"). Lactose is not absorbed, but the enzyme, *lactase*, in intestinal juice, breaks it down to its glucose and galactose components and these are absorbed.

(Lactose is an odd sugar in one respect: it has hardly any taste, sweet or otherwise. Perhaps this is because it is such a prominent constituent of milk, of which it makes up some 4 per cent. Milk is the chief food of the infant mammal, and it is possible that it is useful to have it a bland and almost tasteless food, so that the infant works up no taste associations that will interfere with his choice of food in later life.)

Before I drop the subject of carbohydrates in the diet, I should say that glucose and fructose occur as individual molecules in certain fruit juices. Glucose is sometimes called *grape sugar* and fructose, *fruit sugar*, for that reason. Again, bees, after collecting nectar, break down the sucrose it contains to glucose and fructose and then secrete the mixture as honey. Fruit or honey, when eaten, supply a certain amount of glucose and fructose which, like water and the mineral ions, can be absorbed through the intestines without further change.

What this all boils down to, however, is this: although the body receives carbohydrates into the alimentary canal in various forms, only glucose, fructose and galactose (with glucose making up the bulk) get through the intestinal membranes. Furthermore, within the intestinal cells, fructose and galactose are converted to glucose (the body can rearrange the hydrogen atoms without much trouble), and it is only glucose that gets out of the cells and into the blood stream.

The entire process of carbohydrate digestion and absorption ends with that fact: that glucose and only glucose ends up in the blood. Glucose is, for that reason, sometimes called *blood sugar*.

Once in the blood stream, the glucose dissolves in the blood plasma and is carried by the blood to all the cells of the body, just as oxygen is carried in the red cells. The body cells help themselves to whatever glucose and oxygen they need and by combining the two form carbon dioxide, water and energy. Glucose is the immediate fuel of the body cells and the blood is the conveyor belt carrying that fuel, and oxygen, past them as though they were a line of diners in a cafeteria, each of whom may help himself to as much as he needs but, as would not necessarily be true of human diners, no more than he needs.

But there is a significant difference in the nature of the supply of the oxygen on the one hand and the glucose fuel on the other. You breathe sixteen times a minute so that the oxygen supply is constantly renewed in small spurts and the blood content of the gas remains reasonably steady. You eat, however, only three times a day (on the average) and at irregular times, at that. After a meal, glucose floods the blood stream, while at other times, little or no glucose may enter the blood for hours or even days at a time.

Either extreme has the seeds of fatality in it. Too little glucose would obviously starve the cells, and too much would turn blood into a thick syrup that would not flow. Neither extreme is allowed to occur and for that we can thank our liver.

Here's how it works. The various capillaries that penetrate the intestinal villi carry their gathering load of glucose into a large vessel called the *portal vein*. Through this vein, the blood passes to the liver. There the portal vein breaks up into numerous small twisting branches that are larger than capillaries and are called *sinusoids*. In this way, the blood is forced to work its way through every part of the liver by way of complicated, twisting passages.

To get through the liver under those circumstances takes some time, and while the blood is making its passage, the liver cells have a chance to absorb most of the glucose out of the blood. Once through the liver, the blood collects into another vessel called the *hepatic vein,* which leads into the inferior vena cava and by way of that into the heart from where it joins the general circulation.

The blood, once it leaves the liver, contains just the right concentration of glucose for the body's needs. This "right amount" is about nine-tenths of a gram of glucose per liter of blood or about 5 grams of glucose in the entire adult blood supply.

This may not strike you as very much and, since 5 grams is something less than one-fifth of an ounce, it isn't. The adult human body uses up an absolute minimum of 1,700 kilocalories of energy every day. If you have a desk job, you routinely use up 2,500 kilocalories per day; if you are engaged in manual labor, 4,000 kilocalories or more.

Well, 5 grams of glucose, if entirely consumed, would yield about 20 kilocalories. This is enough to keep you going only for 10 or 15 minutes, even at light work, and no more. Of course, for a while, the intestine keeps passing on fresh glucose to the blood, some of which will survive liver absorption, so that you keep on going. But sooner or later the digestion of a meal is over and the glucose supply stops. It may be hours, days or even weeks before the next meal and yet the blood glucose remains fairly steady. How is that? Well, to begin with, the liver, it should be noted, performs a two-way job. It not only absorbs, it gives out.

As long as the blood in the portal vein is loaded with glucose because of the digestion of a recent meal, the liver keeps taking glucose out of the blood. It uses some of the glucose for its own needs but most of it, it simply stores. It cannot store the glucose as glucose or as any soluble compound because if it did, the soluble compound would float around the liver cell and get in the way of its normal chemical workings.

Rather, the glucose must be converted into some insoluble substance that can, so to speak, be stacked in a corner of the cell, out of the way of trouble. To do this, the liver cell condenses the glucose molecules into a large starchlike string. This is, in fact, sometimes called *animal starch,* though the proper name for it is *glycogen.*

While good times last, more and more glycogen is stored in the liver cells in the form of little starchy granules. But then, there comes a time when the food has all been digested and absorbed and the intestines are, at least temporarily, empty. Blood coming from the intestinal capillaries through the portal vein is no longer gorged with glucose. In fact, it is quite low in glucose, because it has been everywhere else in the body and all the cells have been helping themselves.

When this glucose-short blood starts working its way through the sinusoids of the liver, the glycogen-storage process goes into reverse. The glycogen molecules in the liver cell start breaking apart into glucose, which finds its way through the liver cell membrane and into the blood. Just enough glucose is fed into the blood stream to keep the glucose content of the blood, as it leaves the liver, up to the mark, no more, no less. (The name "glycogen," incidentally, comes from Greek words meaning "sweetness producer.")

And so it goes; after each meal, the liver builds up and stores glycogen; between meals glycogen breaks down; and the result is that the blood level of glucose stays constant. There is actually more to the story than this, but there'll be time later to continue it.

Both glycogen buildup and glycogen breakdown are brought about in several steps, each under the supervision of a separate enzyme. So often do all the enzymes mesh in neat efficiency that we tend to take the intricate chemical processes of the body for granted. However, on the rare occasions when one of the enzymes is missing, we can see the rather terrifying consequences.

For instance, one of the key enzymes in the breakdown of glycogen to glucose is an enzyme called *glucose-6-phosphatase.* Every once in a rare while a child is born without the ability to manufacture enough of that enzyme for its needs. Such a child can store glycogen normally, but can't break it down normally. The liver is gradually engorged with glycogen, and the condition is known as *glycogen storage disease.*

The child's body tries to get round this. It lives on glucose straight from the intestine. It gets glucose out of glycogen stored elsewhere than in the liver, in the muscles, for instance.

In general, though, the usual end is early death; how early depends on how severe the enzyme deficiency is. If the deficiency is very mild, the patient may survive to maturity and even improve thereafter. In most cases, though, death comes before puberty.

Another example of this type of disease, one that is also rare, occurs when infants are born without the ability to manufacture one of the enzymes that control the conversion of galactose to glucose in the intestinal cells. Since infants live primarily on milk, this introduces immediate complications. The sugar of milk, lactose, is digested into its two constituent halves, glucose and galactose, and both are absorbed. Lacking the ability to do anything to the galactose, that sugar must be allowed to enter the blood as such. This condition is called *galactosemia*.

With galactose flooding the blood stream and, by way of that, entering the cells of the body, troubles ensue. Galactose is quite similar to glucose, and enzymes that are intended to work with glucose may easily attach themselves to galactose by mistake. The enzyme-galactose combination is a useless one, but meanwhile the enzyme is taken up and cannot combine with glucose as it should.

Galactose, in thus competing with glucose for the use of the enzyme, cuts down or "inhibits" the enzyme's proper action. Such a process of enzyme-interference is called *competitive inhibition*.

The loss of one enzyme results, you see, in the malfunction of many enzymes and so the symptoms of galactosemia are diverse. For instance, cataracts develop in the eye for some reason. More easily understood is the effect on the brain. Of all the tissues, brain is most dependent on glucose and can least tolerate interference with the enzymes handling it. In galactosemia there is therefore brain damage and consequent mental retardation.

Fortunately, if the symptoms are detected early, and if milk is then withdrawn from the diet, all may be well. Milk is the only food containing galactose.

Yets these are rare conditions. In the vast majority of human beings, all the enzymes are present and all are working. But even granting that all is well with the enzymes, what controls their overall balance? What keeps them working as an efficient unit, shifting in the glycogen-storage direction or in the glycogen-breakdown direction as necessary.

As is almost invariably the case, the answer to such a question invloves a hormone.

The pancreas is a comparatively large gland which I have already mentioned in connection with digestion. It forms pancreatic juice, which is discharged through a duct into the small intestine. If the pancreas were removed from the body, one would expect considerable interference with digestion, but perhaps nothing more dangerous than that. However, in 1889, two German physiologists removed the pancreas of a dog and found that, digestion apart, the animal promptly developed a fatal disorder that looked very much like a human disease well-known since ancient times.

This disease is one of those grouped under the heading of "diabetes" because it involved an over-production of urine (see Chapter 8). The urine in this particular disease had an unusual sweetness to it and 1,500 years ago, an Indian physician noted that such urine collected ants and flies. The disease is therefore called *diabetes mellitus* ("mellitus" coming from the Greek word for "honey"). It is the most common variety of diabetic disease and is the one meant when the word "diabetes" is used alone.

People with diabetes mellitus suffer from increased hunger and thirst, yet lose weight anyway, grow increasingly weak, suffer from an increased tendency to infection, have a host of other troubles, and eventually, die. Starvation diets will increase their life expectancy a bit and prior to thirty years ago this was the only hope.

When it was found that cutting out the pancreas caused diabetes in dogs, attention was concentrated on that gland, and on one part of it in particular.

Earlier, in 1869, a German physiologist, named Paul Langerhans, had discovered in the pancreas unusual cells, existing as separate "islands," surrounded on all sides by ordinary pancreas cells. Each island was small, with a diameter of only about 100 microns, so that even though the average pancreas contains about two million of these cell-islands, they make up altogether only about 1 per cent of the weight of the pancreas. These islands of cells are called today by the remarkably romantic-sounding name of the *Islets of Langerhans.*

The Islets were suspected because the rest of the pancreas seemed innocent. It is possible to tie up the pancreatic duct so that the flow of pancreatic juice is stopped while the pancreas itself is left in place within the animal body. This interferes with digestion but does not cause diabetes. Furthermore, most of the pancreas degenerates with disuse under such conditions, but the Islets are not affected. Whatever they're doing, they're still doing it.

In the early 1900's it was suggested that the Islets formed a gland within a gland, so to speak, and that this inner gland, unlike the main portion of the pancreas, was ductless and formed a hormone which controlled the manipulation of carbohydrate in the body. A name was even suggested for the hormone, *insulin,* from the Latin word for "island."

This was readily accepted. It seemed obvious then that diabetics were people who, at some time during life, found themselves unable to manufacture enough insulin for their needs. If then, insulin could be extracted from the pancreases of domestic animals slaughtered for food, this might be administered to patients and all might be well.

The trick was to get the insulin out of the pancreas before it was destroyed by the digestive enzymes also present in the pancreas. Two Canadians, F. G. Banting, and C. H. Best managed this in 1922 by tying off the pancreas and allowing the digestive portions of the gland to degenerate to harmlessness before trying to soak out the insulin. The hormone thus became commercially available and Banting won the Nobel Prize for Medicine in 1923 as a consequence.

Now insulin is the most important regulator of the chemical reactions that maintain the glucose balance in the blood. The discharge of insulin into the blood by the Islets of Langerhans causes a drop in the blood's glucose concentration. It drops because some of the glucose is absorbed by liver cells and stored as glycogen, while some is absorbed by other cells and used for energy. If the Islets withhold insulin, the reverse situation takes place. Liver and other cells cut down on their glucose absorption and the glucose concentration in blood rises.

Here we have a case of feedback again (see Chapter 9). A high glucose level in the blood stimulates the secretion of additional insulin; down goes the glucose. If it goes down too far, the low concentration of glucose in the blood passing through the pancreas inhibits the secretion of insulin; up goes the glucose.

To make the balance even more delicate, a second hormone

is involved, one that is also secreted by the Islets of Langerhans. The Islets are made up of two distinct kinds of cells, named simply the *alpha cells* and the *beta cells* from the first two letters of the Greek alphabet. It is the beta cells, as it turns out, that produce insulin. The alpha cells turn out a hormone called glucagon.

Glucagon opposes the effect of insulin, so that you have two hormonal forces reacting to the concentration of glucose in the blood and pushing in opposite directions. The Islet cells respond to glucose concentration in the blood by giving one or the other hormone a little the better of the deal in just such a way as to cause the glucose level to move in the right direction.

Why then say, as I have, that insulin is the most important regulator of the glucose balance when it is only one of two? (Actually, it is probably only one of three, since there is a pituitary hormone that seems to have properties like glucagon and joins in keeping the balance.) The reason is a purely human one. It is the insulin supply that goes wrong, not that of the other hormone or hormones, and it is therefore with the the insulin that human beings concern themselves.

In the diabetic, the Islets have lost the ability to turn out sufficient insulin for their needs. The glucose-lowering effect is lost, so that the glucose concentration in blood drifts upward. If the level reaches a certain concentration (about 50 per cent higher than the normal concentration, usually) the *renal threshold* is reached. So much glucose is pushing through the kidney cells and into the tubules that not all of it can be reabsorbed. (And this is just as well, because if the glucose level in blood goes too high it can do damage.) The result is that glucose appears in the urine and although in this way the kidney is acting as a safety valve, it is also a sign of the inefficiency with which the body is handling glucose.

In extreme conditions, the glucose in the urine is present in sufficient quantity to make the urine noticeably sweet. The diabetes has become obviously "mellitus."

Under the circumstances, one way of checking for the presence of diabetes is to test the urine for sugar. For instance, a few drops of urine could be heated with *Benedict's solution,* which, among other things, contains copper sulfate and is a deep blue in color in consequence. If glucose is not present in the urine, the solution remains blue. If glucose is present, the copper sulfate is converted to cuprous oxide during the few minutes of heating. Cuprous oxide is a brick-red insoluble substance which drifts down to the bottom of the tube. The blue color is destroyed and there is no mistaking such a "positive result."

Nowadays an even simpler method is available. Test papers are manufactured, small strips about two inches long, which are impregnated with two enzymes, *glucose dehydrogenase* and *peroxidase,* plus an organic substance called *ortho-tolidine.* If such a strip is dipped into a sample of urine which does not contain glucose, nothing happens. The paper remains its original yellowish color.

What happens if glucose is present? Owing to the presence of glucose dehydrogenase on the paper, the glucose present in the urine undergoes a combination with oxygen in the air, and hydrogen peroxide is formed. In the presence of the peroxidase on the paper, the hydrogen peroxide then combines with the ortho-tolidine, also on the paper, to form a deep blue compound. All this sounds complicated, but what it amounts to is that a test paper is plunged into urine and if it turns blue the owner of the urine is in trouble.

This new paper strip test is even more reliable than the older Benedict's solution variety. It is occasionally possible for the urine to contain some compound which is not glucose and which has nothing to do with diabetes, but which can change copper sulfate to cuprous oxide. The result is a "false positive." The chances of false positives with the paper strip test are virtually nil.

Urine is tested for sugar routinely when people apply for insurance or when they are being drafted into the army. The medical profession urges us to have it tested periodically anyway. Diabetes is the most common of the *metabolic disorders* and may strike anyone at any time, though there is a tendency for it to run in families.

The word *metabolism* refers to sum total of the chemical reactions going on in living tissue, so a metabolic disorder is one that involves body chemistry directly. Unlike the infectious diseases, in which body chemistry is involved indirectly through the interference of some invading micro-organism metabolic diseases cannot be "caught." On the other hand, neither can we be vaccinated against them. With the advent of antibiotics and modern insecticides, infectious diseases have declined in importance and metabolic disorders have become the physician's main concern.

Diabetes, like so many abnormal conditions, is more easily handled if it is caught early. If it is, there is a fighting chance that proper diet and exercise may control it without the necessity of insulin. For this purpose, diagnosis by urine tests is insufficient. By the time blood glucose has passed the renal threshold and is spilling over into the urine, diabetes is fairly advanced.

A more delicate test is the *glucose tolerance test.* In a healthy human being, the glucose level in the blood rises a little after a meal (with glucose flooding into the portal vein) but quickly falls to normal levels as the raised glucose stimulates additional insulin secretion. In a person on the edge of diabetes, however, the raised glucose level after a meal falls more slowly because insulin is being produced more sluggishly.

This effect can be exaggerated by feeding a person a quantity of glucose solution on an empty stomach. The glucose level in blood goes up faster and higher and the Islets must work harder to bring it down. Blood samples are taken before the "glucose meal" and afterwards at timed intervals. In the normal person blood glucose is at normal levels, despite the glucose meal, within two hours. If the glucose level stays high for three hours or more, the patient is probably in the early stages of diabetes.

Fat people sometimes show a diabetic pattern when they undergo one of these tests and return to normal once they lose weight. On the other hand, the incidence of diabetes among overweights is greater than among people of normal weight. This is one of the dangers involved in doing yourself too proud at the table day after day, and not the worst, either.

Diabetics cannot be cured. That is, there is no known way of causing the Islets of Langerhans to function again once they have quite ceased to do so. However, a diabetic can live a reasonably normal life and be relieved of some of the distressing symptoms of diabetes, if he is supplied with an outside source of insulin.

Insulin therapy has its difficulties. There is as much danger in too much insulin as in too little, since the glucose level in blood must not be allowed to sink too low, either. Too much insulin, and therefore too little glucose in the blood, will cause unconsciousness (*insulin shock*), and a diabetic is urged to carry a supply of sugar so that he can take some quickly if he feels the symptoms of shock coming.

The amount of insulin needed by a particular patient depends upon the amount still being supplied by his limping Islets and must be carefully determined under a physician's care. Special preparations of insulin are usually used to keep it from taking action too quickly. If combined with some inactive protein, it will only work as it slowly breaks away from the protein and thus the insulin is used more evenly over a longer period of time.

The patient must watch his diet carefully, even to the point of weighing what he eats, since if he eats too much or too little, he alters his insulin requirement. Eating too much is the greater danger and, in fact, in countries with low standards of living, where semi-starvation is the rule, there is a lower incidence of diabetes. And in countries with a high standard of living where there is a temporary lowering of standards because of war—as in Great Britain in the early 1940's—there is also a lowering of diabetes incidence. Diabetes is one of the few metabolic diseases which is more likely to strike women than men, but no one knows why.

All this illustrates the delicacy and convenience of the body machinery when it is working correctly. From moment to moment, in the healthy person, the insulin supply is being adjusted by the Islets to suit the glucose level. If we try the adjustment by hand, so to speak, once the body's automation fails, the results (though far, far better than nothing, of course) are tedious and risky in comparison.

One of the tedious factors of insulin therapy is that the preparation must be injected. That means hypodermic needles, sterilization punctures, discomfort. Matters would be much simpler if the insulin could be swallowed. Unfortunately, that is quite out of the question. The insulin molecule is that of a small protein and in the alimentary canal it is quickly digested and put out of action.

Insulin substitutes, which might be simple enough to resist digestion and yet do the direct work of insulin, seem also to be out of the question, at least so far. A group of British chemists, under the direction of Frederick Sanger, began an onslaught on the insulin molecule in an attempt to learn its exact structure. They used the same general methods already described in Chapter 7 in connection with the amino acid structure of the hemoglobins. In fact, it was Sanger's group that perfected these methods.

By 1953, the investigation was successful. The smallest possible version of the insulin molecule is made up of forty-eight amino acids and the exact position of each of these in the molecule was worked out. Unfortunately, at that point biochemists are still stumped. There is nothing in the molecular structures that suggests something simpler that might do the job. And so far, any change in the insulin molecule beyond the most trivial, even those that leave it about as complicated as it is, destroys its workings. The biochemists seem stymied.

However, there is one other attack on the problem from a completely different direction that has raised hopes for oral therapy in at least some cases. A hormone, you see, must not only be produced in a hurry on demand, it must be destroyed in a hurry on demand, also. If the glucose level in blood drops and the Islets cut down on insulin production in consequence, the result is a rise in glucose concentration. The quickness of the response is, however, held back by the fact that there is still insulin in the blood and tissues that had been previously secreted by the Islets. If this "old" insulin could be destroyed at the same time that "new" insulin is being cut down on, the quickness and delicacy of response would be increased.

This destruction of "old" insulin is carried out under the influence of an enzyme called *insulinase*. Now, patients who are producing insufficient insulin can't be made to produce more insulin by any treatment we know today, but they might be kept from destroying what insulin they do produce, if some substance can be found which will cut down on the activity of insulinase without interfering too seriously with too many other enzymes.

Such insulinase-inhibiting substances have been found and are being tested thoroughly. They are absorbed into the body unchanged if eaten, so they can be taken orally. They can be synthesized without too much trouble, so that we won't be so dependent upon the supply of animals being slaughtered (each having only one pancreas, of course). It only remains to be certain that there is no long-term damage to the body.

Of course, for such "diabetes pills" to work, the body must

produce at least some insulin. This is usually the case with people who develop diabetes in mature life. Diabetes that develops in childhood is usually more severe and often no insulin at all can be detected in such patients. For them, inhibiting insulinase would do no good and nothing is even on the horizon yet that will replace the hypodermic.

I have already said that insulin apparently encourages the passage of glucose from the blood into the cells. There are two general theories as to how insulin manages to do this. One theory is that insulin affects a particular enzyme reaction.

For instance, immediately after glucose gets into a cell, it is converted into a compound called *glucose-6-phosphate*. This reaction proceeds under the influence of an enzyme called *glucokinase*. If a tissue extract containing this enzyme is supplied with glucose and other necessary ingredients, glucose disappears and glucose-6-phosphate takes its place. If a bit of insulin is also added, this happens much more quickly.

Insulin, then, apparently accelerates the action of glucokinase, or perhaps it neutralizes the effect of another hormone which is inhibiting glucokinase; the result is the same. Once the glucose-6-phosphate is formed within a liver cell, it can be changed by several steps into glycogen and stored. If it is formed within other cells, it can be changed by a number of steps into carbon dioxide and water, and the chemical energy so obtained may be put to a number of uses.

In either case, glucose disappears rapidly from within the cell and more glucose must diffuse into the cell from the blood just as rapidly.

If, however, insulin is in short supply, the glucokinase is working poorly and glucose-6-phosphate is formed slowly. With the glucose within the cell disappearing but slowly, additional glucose enters the cell from the blood as slowly. Glucose piles up in the blood and all the symptoms of diabetes appear.

There are other biochemists, a minority at present, I believe, who consider insulin to have a more general function. They believe the cell membrane to be something more than a passive boundary between the cell and the outside world; something more than a barrier with sub-microscopic holes in it, through which some molecules will work their way and some won't.

In the previous chapter, in talking of sodium and potassium ions, I pointed out that most of the potassium ions ended up inside the cell, while most of the sodium ions remained outside the cell, even though both could freely pass through the cell membrane.

Apparently, the cell has ways of allowing one molecule or ion through its membrane while another, of about the same size, is stopped. Furthermore a molecule or ion may be allowed through in one direction and not in the other. This sort of thing, which invariably takes energy and can't be done by the membrane of a dead cell, is called *active transport*. Some chemists now think that special substances called *permeases* exist in the membrane, which bring about this one-way passage.

Now it is certain that glucose enters cells by means of active transport. It is absorbed into the intestinal cell from the alimentary canal, for instance, much more rapidly than other sugars of similar, or even slightly smaller, molecular size. Presumably it gets into cells from the blood stream with similar rapidity and ease.

The means used for the purpose may be the change to glucose-6-phosphate within the cell, which results in the entry of additional glucose, as I have already said. Biochemists favoring the minority theory, however, hold that the rapid absorption of glucose depends on the nature of the cell membrane. They say that insulin molecules adhere to the membrane and change its properties. Membrane-plus-insulin can pull glucose through quickly (active transport); membrane-minus-insulin lets glucose enter by passive diffusion merely, which is relatively slow.

I have a personal preference for this second theory, for the reason that, if it were true, it could afford a general explanation for the workings of any hormone. Any hormone by coating the membrane of some cells might govern the rate at which various substances could enter and leave the cell, and by so doing could control the chemistry of the cell very easily.

Of course, to make the membrane theory stick, it would be nice if we were sure about the structure of the cell membrane; if we knew why a hormone might coat one cell and not another; if we could tell exactly how a membrane brought about active transport and how a hormone coating might change its ability to do that. None of that is, as yet, quite within the scientific grasp, but life would be dull if all problems vanished.

Chapter 11

Proteins Floating Freely

AT THE BEGINNING of the previous chapter, I presented the organic compounds of food divided into three classes. I talked about one of those classes, the carbohydrates, in that chapter. A second class of compounds, the proteins, is a logical one to follow, because it is handled by the body in a way parallel to that in which carbohydrates are handled.

Protein molecules are, for the most part, very large and can be broken up by the action of acid or enzymes into quite small units. This is similar to what starch or cellulose, large molecules of the carbohydrate class, undergo with similar treatment. However, starch and cellulose are broken up into a single type of unit, glucose. Proteins, on the other hand, are broken up into a number of different units. Most of these units (in the case of some proteins, all of them) fall into a single group of compounds, the *amino acids,* already mentioned in Chapter 7. Nineteen different amino acids are of common occurrence in proteins.

The naturally-occurring amino acids all contain nitrogen atoms in their molecules in addition to the usual carbon, hydrogen and oxygen. Three of them contain sulfur atoms in addition. All the amino acids share certain broad properties, but differ in details. The molecule of each amino acid contains a central carbon atom to which is attached, on one side, an *amine group,* made up of a nitrogen atom and two hydrogens, which has basic properties; and on the other side, a *carboxyl group,* made up of a carbon atom, two oxygens and a hydrogen, which has acid properties. It is from this fact, that the name "amino acid" is derived. This same central carbon atom is also attached in a third direction to a single hydrogen atom, and in a fourth and final direction to a more or less complicated group of atoms called a *side-chain.* It is this side-chain which is different in each of the nineteen varieties of amino acid.

The various amino acids can be hooked together by having the amine group of one condense with the carboxyl group of another. A double amino acid arising from the condensation of two amino acids would still have a carboxyl group free at one end and an amine group at the other. It could continue to condense at both ends. This always holds true no matter how many amino acids condense, as long as the two ends of the long line of amino acids that is formed do not condense together to form a closed circle and end the process.

A series of amino acids condensed together form a chain from which the various side-chains stick out. Each side-chain has its own chemical properties, and the properties of the chain of amino acids as a whole depend on the exact pattern presented by the various side-chains. This, in turn, depends upon the order in which the amino acids are condensed. Each different order presents a different pattern of side-chains and, therefore, somewhat different properties for the chain as a whole.

The number of different orders in which hundreds and thousands of amino acids can be condensed is quite unbelievable. A protein molecule consisting of only one of each of the nineteen amino acids could be built up in over 120, 000,000,-000,000,000 different ways. And yet in actual fact amino acids condense into single molecules containing not twenty, but literally hundreds and thousands of the individual units.

It is no surprise then that countless different proteins exist; that every species of creature has its own distinctive proteins; that every individual may use thousands of different proteins for thousands of different jobs; that proteins (and certain allied compounds) are complex enough to account for all the flexibilities and subtleties and versatilities of life. Even very minor differences in amino acid arrangements can have vital effects on the body as I pointed out in Chapter 7.

It also means that even if the proteins of food could be absorbed into the body intact (which they can't be, their molecules being too large), they would do us no good. Ox protein is not human protein and, for that matter, grass protein is not ox protein. In fact, if the digestive system is bypassed and if foreign protein is injected into the blood stream, considerable harm and even death might result. This will be further discussed in a later chapter.

However, if the protein molecules of the food are pulled apart into the individual amino acids, and if these are then absorbed and put together again in a different order appropriate to the needs of the feeder, all will be well. And that is exactly what happens.

Once in the stomach, food is mixed with the strongly acid gastric juice. The acid itself hydrolyzes protein molecules slowly, but in addition the gastric juice contains an enzyme called pepsin which accelerates the hydrolysis of the protein at certain points.

Two neighboring amino acids in the chain (or chains) of condensed amino acids are connected by what is called a *peptide link*. Ordinary acid such as that in the stomach will hydrolyze any peptide link, but pepsin will only bring about the hydrolysis of the links between certain amino acids, but not between others.

Between these different actions of acid and pepsin, protein molecules leave the stomach and enter the small intestine split up into fragmented but still rather large chains of amino acids. (Amino acid chains that are relatively small compared to those in proteins are called peptides.)

In the first stretch of the small intestine, the peptides are mixed with pancreatic juice, which contains two enzymes that, like pepsin, are *proteases,* that is, they catalyze the hydrolysis of the peptide links in proteins. These two enzymes are *trypsin* and *chymotrypsin*. Like pepsin, each of these brings about the hydrolysis only of certain peptide links. However, the peptide links which are broken by trypsin and chymotrypsin are not those which pepsin can handle. What's more, the links trypsin will split are not the same as those chymotrypsin will split.

The result is that peptide links which rode out the storm with impunity while they had only pepsin and the slow-acting stomach acid to contend with, now fall rapidly before the onslaughts of trypsin and chymotrypsin. Before the food has passed very far down the length of the small intestine, the peptide chains have been cut down to lengths of two, three or four amino acids.

The intestinal juice itself contains a wide variety of *cathepsins,* which are enzymes particularly designed to work on these small peptides; and at this stage, the proteins are broken down to individual amino acids at last. These, finally, are absorbed.

(Remember, by the way, that all the different enzymes mentioned in this book, together with thousands that are not, are protein molecules. All are made up of the same amino acids, but in different proportions and in different orders. And each enzyme has its own special abilities. This is an excellent example of the inherent versatility of the protein molecule, which I mentioned earlier in the chapter.)

After a meal, amino acids flood into the portal vein just as glucose does. The amino acid content of blood just about doubles after a meal when compared with the level during a fast. Nor does the level return to fasting value for about six hours after a meal.

However, the amount of uncondensed amino acids in the blood generally remains quite low in comparison with the amount that enters the portal vein, because in the liver the amino acids (like glucose) are absorbed and changed. Just as glucose units are there condensed to form giant glycogen molecules, so amino acid units are condensed to form giant protein molecules.

There follows a difference, though. Whereas most of the glucose is held back by the liver and stored in the form of glycogen, the liver does not store protein. In fact, there is no definite point in the body where protein is stored and sits around waiting for emergencies. All protein is working one way or another at all times.

The protein formed by the liver out of the amino acids reaching it through the portal vein is poured back into the blood, where it remains dissolved in the plasma. This is therefore called *plasma protein.* (These are not the only proteins in blood. Remember hemoglobin, which is also part of the blood and the most common protein in it. However, hemoglobin is imprisoned in the red cell, so to speak. The plasma proteins float freely, dissolved in the watery portion of the blood. No cell walls restrain them.)

The plasma protein circulates to all cells of the body and, like glucose, is there for the taking by each cell. The individual cell absorbs it as needed, breaks it down to amino acids, and rebuilds these into the particular variety of proteins that suits its own needs.

But then, if the liver does not store protein, how does it prevent too much plasma protein from being poured into the blood? Where are the delicate controls that were present in the case of glucose? (The chance of protein overproduction is not as great as glucose overproduction, since protein supply in food is less apt to be excessive than is carbohydrate. In general, high-protein food is more expensive than low-protein food, and therefore is less commonly eaten.)

The answer to possible over-intake of protein is simple. The liver can take the excess amino acids and subject them to chemical changes that remove the nitrogen atoms and convert them to urea. It pours the urea into the blood, which carries it to the kidney and out of the body as I explained in Chapter 8.

What is left over of each amino acid, after nitrogen is removed, is a fragment containing carbon, hydrogen and oxygen atoms only. This fragment can be broken down to carbon dioxide, water and energy; or it can be built up first to glucose, then to glycogen, in which form it can be stored. This process is called *glyconeogenesis* (from Greek words meaning "birth of new sugar," because it represents the formation of glycogen—which can give rise to sugar—out of something that, originally, was not sugar).

On the other hand, suppose that the supply of protein is less than what is needed. What happens then?

Well, all the protein of the body is working, but each tissue has more protein molecules on the job than, in a pinch, it really needs. In case of emergency, with food short, each tissue sacrifices protein molecules in order of dispensability. The more important types of proteins are kept in existence at the expense of some of the less important ones.

In the process, the tissues waste away, but so carefully does the body ration its protein supply and so shrewdly does it conserve what is important, that people have fasted totally for periods of weeks, or lived on less than minimum supplies of protein for months and survived. Some of the human wrecks uncovered in the Nazi concentration camps by the

Allied armies had been reduced to skeleton proportions, yet, with care, they survived and were brought back to reasonably normal health.

But naturally, if protein deprivation is carried too far, death is the only result.

Of course, you may wonder why it is necessary to convert the amino acids into protein if there is no question of storage. Glucose is converted to glycogen in order to form an insoluble substance that can be tucked away in the cells till needed. But the plasma proteins are soluble and are deliberately put back into the blood. Why not leave them in the original form of amino acids, ship the mixture about in that form and let the cells help themselves?

In one respect this would be a far simpler alternative, since there must be a problem in getting the comparatively large plasma protein molecules from liver cells into the blood and from the blood into the tissue cells. With the much smaller amino acid molecules there is no trouble at all in this respect.

There are a number of reasons, though, for the existence of plasma proteins, and I will take them up one at a time.

In the first place, the plasma proteins are not simple collections of amino acids tied together in a first-come-first-served fashion. They contain certain proportions of each of the approximately twenty amino acids. The liver fashions them in careful design, so to speak.

It is important that the tissue cells receive not just a random mixture of amino acids but the desired quantity, not too much and not too little, of each. If the amino acids were present in the blood in their own form and in no other way, one can visualize each tissue cell trying desperately to collect some of this, some of that, and a little of the other. It would not be efficient and, somehow, it strikes me as being undignified.

Instead, the liver cells (the versatile and unbelievably busy maids-of-all-work of the body) carefully string amino acids together in proper proportions and send out, so to speak, a complete well-balanced and neatly packaged meal for the cells.

Of course, this means that the liver cells must find enough of each amino acid in the supply that reaches them through the portal vein. There are proteins which will supply all the amino acids in reasonably good proportions. The proteins of milk, meat and eggs are excellent in this respect. Some of the grain proteins are also good.

On the other hand, there are some proteins which are deficient in some of the amino acids. Gelatin and some of the plant proteins are the most familiar examples.

Within limits, the liver can fix things up. If there is too much of amino acid A and too little of amino acid B, it can convert A to B and restore the balance. But even the liver is not all-powerful.

The fact is that some amino acids cannot be formed by the hard-working liver, no matter what other amino acids are supplied it. These unformable amino acids must be present in the food to begin with or we simply have to do without, like it or not. These are the *dietarily essential amino acids*.

The existence of this situation was first discovered when rats fed on certain proteins such as zein (a protein in corn) lost weight and died although plenty of zein and carbohydrates and everything else was supplied (everything else, that is, but other proteins). If a little milk protein were added to the diet, though, before it was too late, the rats recovered and grew again. The zein, it seems, lacks certain dietarily essential amino acids, which the milk protein supplies.

Similar and more delicate experiments have been carried out on human beings. The subjects were graduate students who were studying under the nutritionists carrying out the experiments and who—I suppose—volunteered. The students were put on rigidly controlled diets, which contained ample supplies of water, carbohydrates, fat, minerals and vitamins. Instead of protein, however, they were fed on various mixtures of purified amino acids.

Now let's see what the nutritionists could do with such an experiment. Obviously, they couldn't wait and see which students deprived of which amino acids sickened and died. There had to be something they could catch at long before such a point was reached.

Under ordinary conditions, tissue protein is continually breaking down with the wear and tear of living. Consequently there is always a minimum amount of urea in the urine. If enough protein is coming in through the diet, the protein coming in will replace that protein loss.

The amount of protein coming in to the body is measured by analyzing samples of the food for nitrogen (since the nitrogen atoms in food are almost entirely in the protein molecules) and subtracting the nitrogen content of the feces (since that represents protein that was not absorbed and therefore never entered the body). The amount of protein leaving the body is measured by analyzing the urine for nitrogen (since here the nitrogen is almost entirely in the urea molecules, which are derived from the body protein being worn out in the course of daily living).

When income equals outgo the person is said to be in *nitrogen balance*. This is usually the case in adequately-nourished adults. If they should happen to take in more protein than they need, the excess is stripped down to carbohydrate and the nitrogen is excreted as urea, so that outgo zooms up to match the too-high income.

In the case of children who are growing and are therefore continuously laying down new protein (or adults who are doing the same after having survived semi-starvation or a wasting disease), the nitrogen income is greater than the nitrogen outgo. They are gaining protein and are in *positive nitrogen balance*. (This is poor naming since they are not in balance, but this is what the nutritionists call it and nothing can be done about it now.)

In the case of people who are living on less than the minimum necessary amount of protein, outgo is greater than income and they are in *negative nitrogen balance*.

Now to return to our graduate students on their amino-acid-mixture diets. If all the amino acids are supplied in the proper proportion, they remain in nitrogen balance. But what happens if one of the amino acids is left out completely?

If the omitted amino acid is any one of eleven particular ones, nothing at all happens. With the other amino acids present in ample supply, the liver makes what it needs of the missing amino acid (or of all eleven, if all eleven are missing), and all is as before.

It happens, sometimes, though, that a particular amino acid is left out of the diet which the liver cannot make. When this happens, the liver cannot make protein. It can't put the remaining amino acids together and leave holes where the missing amino acid ought to be for later insertion. (It would be nice if it could, but it can't tie up its chemical machinery waiting for the missing unit.) So it has to strip nitrogen off the whole lot of incoming amino acid, eliminate it as urea and convert what is left of the amino acids into glycogen. An alternative might be to get supplies of the missing amino acid from body proteins, but this would mean discarding whole protein molecules just to get one kind of amino acid. The other amino acids would be stripped and urea excreted.

In either case, the graduate student, missing one of the crucial amino acids cannot replace the protein lost in wear and tear and goes into negative nitrogen balance. The giveaway, therefore, that a particular amino acid is dietarily essential is the appearance of a negative nitrogen balance.

By such methods it has been decided that eight of the amino acids are dietarily essential to adult human beings.

This may not be the situation in children. Children are always in positive nitrogen balance, if well-fed, and need more of each amino acid per pound weight than do adults. An adult liver might be able to make a given amino acid at the rate suitable for an adult, even in the total absence of a dietary supply; yet an infant liver might perhaps not be able to keep up the supply of that amino acid at a rate that will suffice for the greater needs of the child.

However, nitrogen-balance experiments on youngsters are difficult to carry out and so far we must confine ourselves to speculation. For one thing, few, if any, parents will volunteer their children for the purpose. (I wouldn't volunteer mine.) For another thing (judging by my children) getting youngsters to cooperate on dietary experiments would be next door to impossible.

Quite apart from the fact that plasma proteins supply the amino acids to the cells in properly proportioned packages, they differ from the amino acids in another way. They are composed of large molecules, whereas amino acid molecules are small. This is important, because large molecules have certain properties necessary to the body that small molecules (even if present in proportionately greater number) do not have.

Consider the blood stream as it is driven by the heart. As the heart contracts forcefully, it exerts a strong pressure on the blood it contains, which is therefore squirted energetically into the arteries. The arteries have elastic walls which bulge outward under the force of the blood pulsing through and contract again once the blood current has surged past.

This is the pulse that can be felt wherever an artery approaches close to the skin, notably on the inner surface of the wrist. The expansion and contraction of the artery mirrors the expansion and contraction of the heart. The rapidity and strength of the pulse can give information to the trained observer, but the number of diagnostic aids developed by modern medicine have reduced the relative importance of pulse-taking, even though in the movies there are times when doctors seem to do nothing else.

This *blood pressure,* originating from the contraction of the heart and necessary as the driving force behind the living river of blood, raises complications when the capillaries are reached. The capillary walls are extremely thin; they have to be if materials are to diffuse in and out rapidly.

Well, then, water diffuses out of the capillaries, bathing all the cells. Outside the capillaries, this is called *interstitial fluid.* This interstitial fluid is plasma minus most of its proteins, since the protein molecules are too large to diffuse through the capillary walls. Other smaller molecules such as glucose, mineral ions and urea diffuse through and are found in interstitial fluid as well as in plasma.

The interstitial fluid is not permanently lost to the blood. It collects into vessels, which join up into larger ones. It flows sluggishly through these vessels, impelled by the contraction of nearby muscles (going about their own business). The nearby muscle, as it contracts, squeezes the vessel and the interstitial fluid is forced to move out of that part of the vessel. It can only move in one direction (toward the heart) because the vessel is fitted with one way valves, like the heart itself, and the liquid cannot move backward.

This goes on until the fluid finally enters a large vessel called the *thoracic duct,* which empties into the inferior vena cava (the large vein leading into the heart) and rejoins the blood in this way. The interstitial fluid within the vessels is called *lymph* and the vessels are the *lymphatic ducts.* Lymph contains no formed elements except for a type of white cell called *lymphocytes* (1,000 to 20,000 per cubic millimeter).

Thus, there is a kind of slow circulation in the body in addition to the fast circulation in the blood vessels. The slow circulation consists of fluid leaving the capillaries, bathing the cells and returning.

But blood pressure pushing the fluid out of the capillaries is a stronger force than the erratic muscular pressure nudging the lymph back into the blood stream. The maximum blood pressure, as the blood leaves the heart, is 110 to 150 millimeters of mercury, about a fifth of an atmosphere. As the heart relaxes, the pressure drops to 80 millimeters of mercury. The former is the *systolic pressure* and the latter the *diastolic pressure*.

The systolic pressure is about 40 millimeters of mercury in a new-born baby but this rises rapidly to 80 at the age of one month, then more slowly to 100 by the age of twelve and 120 by seventeen. There is a tendency for a very slow rise thereafter. In cases of *hypertension* ("high blood pressure") the values rise persistently and considerably above normal, reaching up to 300 millimeters of mercury, systolic, and 150, diastolic. Such high pressures strain the heart, can rupture the smaller vessels, damage the kidneys and, generally, shorten life drastically.

If we considered only the blood pressure, liquid would be leaking out of the capillaries faster than the vena cava could bring it back. Interstitial fluid would accumulate and the body would bloat while the blood supply ran short.

To be sure, there are factors which tend to minimize the effects of blood pressure in the capillaries. For one thing, the capillaries may be microscopic, while the arteries are wide (the human aorta is an inch wide); yet, put all together, the capillaries have a cross section 600 to 800 times greater in area than do all the arteries put altogether, so that in the capillaries the blood current slows and the pressure drops. (An analogous effect can be seen when a river rushing between constricting cliff walls broadens out in a flat region.)

Secondly, a portion of the pressure is consumed in overcoming the friction of the blood stream against the walls of the blood vessel. The amount of friction depends upon the *viscosity* of the blood. The more viscous, the more slowly and sluggishly will any liquid flow. (If you have ever tried to pour a viscous liquid like honey or molasses you know what I mean.)

Substances dissolved in water generally increase its viscosity. Large molecules dissolved in it (especially if they are asymmetric, i.e. rod-shaped rather than ball-shaped) do more to increase its viscosity than would the same weight of small molecules. Thus, if a million amino acid molecules were condensed into twenty large and rod-like protein molecules, those protein molecules would do more to increase viscosity than would the original million small amino acid molecules.

The presence of plasma proteins thus helps control blood

flow and blood pressure as amino acids could never do. Here is one way in which plasma protein molecules, by mere size, help the body in ways that amino acids could not.

But the increased cross-sectional area of the capillaries, together with viscosity effects, only minimize the ability of blood pressure to squeeze fluid out of the capillaries. They do not remove it. Something more is required to balance that force.

To find what that something more is, consider the semipermeable membranes once again, that is, specifically, the membranes that bound the thin capillary walls. On one side (the tissue side) is interstitial fluid, made up of water, small ions and molecules, all of which can easily diffuse through the membrane if they should happen to strike it. On the other side (the blood side) is plasma, which contains all that interstitial fluid contains plus protein molecules as well. The protein molecules are too large to diffuse through the membrane.

This puts the plasma at a disadvantage. The interstitial fluid molecules move through the membrane in carefree manner. The small plasma molecules, however, have to make their way (in a manner of speaking) about the giant protein molecules which cannot diffuse through and which remain in the way of those molecules that can.

The result is that there is a greater tendency for molecules to diffuse from the interstitial fluid into the capillaries than vice versa, if blood pressure is ignored. This greater tendency inward is called *osmotic pressure*. It is the osmotic pressure pushing inward that balances the blood pressure pushing outward.

At the arterial end of the capillaries, the blood pressure is a little higher than the osmotic pressure and there is a small tendency for fluid to be forced out of the capillary. At the venous end of the capillaries, the blood pressure has fallen to the point where it is a little lower than the osmotic pressure and there is a small tendency for fluid to re-enter the capillary. On the whole, the two forces balance and the slow leak out of the capillaries at one end is balanced by the slow leak into the capillaries at the other (combined with the lymph movement under muscular pressure).

If the plasma proteins were entirely broken up into amino acids, all the nourishment would still be present and we might be optimistic enough to suppose that the cells might even be able to pick individual amino acids out of the plasma in proper proportions. However, the osmotic effect would be gone. Amino acids would diffuse through the capillary membranes easily so that diffusion would be equal in both directions. There would be no net osmotic pressure inward. Blood pressure would be unopposed and the blood vessels would slowly and fatally deflate like a punctured tire. Again molecular largeness proves to have its special uses.

This combination of osmotic pressure and blood pressure working together is perhaps not an easy thing to visualize. However, those who have battled New York subways during rush hours—or other crowded means of transportation anywhere—have something with which to compare the situation. It is comparatively easy to push into a subway car, since all the people on the platform are pushing to get on simultaneously. It is comparatively hard to push out of the subway car, since there are people in the car who are not getting off at that station and who hang on to the straps with all their might.

If the situation were left to itself then, people would push into the car wildly and those already on who wanted to get off would be out of luck. This net movement inward we might call the "subway osmotic pressure" effect.

To balance the situation, we have subway guards who shout, "Let them off, please" and urge those on the platform to stand to one side till those inside get out. This is the "subway blood pressure" effect. The two effects, working together, fill and empty the cars with reasonable efficiency, considering the crowds.

Failure of the system to work would create chaos in the subway cars. A similar failure would also trouble the body. The collection of excess water in the tissues results in the bloated condition called *edema*. Sometimes edema occurs in localized spots, as around a mosquito bite or bee sting, or, more generally, in response to some allergy. This last condition produces *hives*.

As we all know, hemorrhage can be fatal. What is it, though, that is most serious about blood loss? Actually, the loss of plasma is more dangerous than the loss of red cells. The body contain red cells and hemoglobin in a prudent excess over rock-bottom need, and it can make more quickly and on short notice. The temporary anemia due to hemorrhage need only require some rest and, perhaps, some iron pills and all will be well.

The seriousness of plasma loss is owing to the loss of plasma proteins. This is not because the body lacks a mechanism to replace them quickly. In fact, physiologists have experimented with dogs as follows: a dog is bled in instalments, and the red cells are separated from each instalment of blood. These red cells are mixed with salt water in a concentration adjusted to such a level that it will not harm the cells or the dog. This red-cell-plus-salt-water mixture is restored to the dog's blood vessels. As you see, what has not been restored are the plasma proteins. In this process, called *plasmapheresis*, the plasma proteins in the dog's circulation can be reduced below the normal level and the speed of replacement studied. In such experiments, it turns out that up to one-quarter of the total plasma protein can be replaced in one day.

There is no reason to suppose a human being is not as capable as a dog in this respect. Therefore, if he were to lose one-quarter of his blood supply, he could make up the plasma proteins in a day and certainly his cells could get along, nutritionally speaking, on a somewhat short supply of plasma protein for such a limited time.

The danger is not in undernutrition, however. It is that as the plasma protein goes down during hemorrhage, the osmotic pressure mechanism breaks down. The blood vessels cannot regain the fluid they are losing to the tissues or cannot pull enough fluid in from the tissues to make up for what they have lost in hemorrhage. Either way you look at it, if the process goes too far, the patient dies.

It is for this reason that on the battlefield, patients are often given blood plasma, when "whole blood" of the right blood type is not available. Blood plasma creates no transfusion difficulties since there are no red cells in it to be agglutinated (see Chapter 6); and it supplies what is needed most of all at the moment, plasma protein to keep up blood volume through the osmotic effect. Once that is done, red cell replacement can be carried through more leisurely during the patient's recovery.

At the time of World War II, an important research program was carried on at Harvard Medical School under E. J. Cohn to separate plasma proteins from plasma on a large scale. This was managed by subjecting the blood to temperatures below freezing and then adding ethyl alcohol in various quantities.

Plasma protein is less soluble in alcohol than in water and the addition of alcohol causes it to precipitate out of solution as a solid material, which can then be separated from the liquid and stored. The low temperature during the ethyl alcohol addition is necessary to preserve the fragile protein molecule from the damage that would otherwise be inflicted upon it by the unnatural presence of ethyl alcohol in its vicinity.

But if it is the large size of the plasma protein molecule that keeps the osmotic effect going, and since the body can get along without it as far as nutrition is concerned for the limited time it will need for replacement, why can't other large molecules serve the same purpose? Plasma proteins, after all, must be obtained from blood in the long run and blood is always a difficult item to keep in stock. A large molecule that could be obtained from some more easily available source might be very valuable.

Of course, not any large molecule will do. It must be one that will do no harm to the body if injected into the blood stream, and which will stay in the blood stream a reasonable length of time after insertion and not be eliminated forthwith through the kidneys. Furthermore, the molecule must not be too large or the osmotic effect goes down again.

Such substitute-large-molecules are called *plasma expanders,* because they bring about an expansion in the volume of plasma through osmotic effects. They are more popularly called "blood substitutes," but that is a poor name because they substitute for only one out of the many functions of blood. No plasma expanders have yet been found which are thoroughly satisfactory, but there is some value derived from certain preparations of gelatin: also from *dextran,* which is a starchlike material produced by certain micro-organisms, and *polyvinylpyrrolidone,* which is a large-molecule synthetic substance produced in the laboratory.

Now it is the way of the body never to let any substance do one job if half a dozen can be piled on it. The plasma proteins serve a nutritive function and control the blood's volume by way of their effect on viscosity and osmotic pressure. If that were all they did, they would be important enough. However, more tasks are piled onto them. For instance, as long as they're moving about the body (so the body seems to reason) they might as well be carrying something while they are about it.

The plasma proteins have as an added function, therefore, that of *transport*. Various hormones, as an example, make their way from gland to target organ by taking a ride on plasma proteins.

The most interesting case of such transport, however, involves substances that could not be handled by the blood stream without a protein carrier. To take that up, though, will require a new chapter.

Chapter 12

The Two Phases

PLANTS MAKE THEIR OWN CARBOHYDRATE out of carbon dioxide and water, as I mentioned in passing at the very beginning of the book. This is an energy-consuming process and the plants must get energy somewhere to make carbohydrate production practical.

A complex chemical mechanism, of which the key constituent is a compound called *chlorophyll,* traps some of the visible light of the sun and the energy of that light is used. Since chlorophyll absorbs red and yellow light more strongly than others, it mainly reflects the green and blue portion of sunlight (which is itself a mixture of all colors). It is for this reason that green is so characteristic a color of plants.

This process of manufacturing carbohydrate out of carbon dioxide and water is called *photosynthesis,* from Greek words meaning "put together by light." In the process of photosynthesis, there are a couple of oxygen atoms left over for every molecule of carbon dioxide and of water used. These oxygen atoms combine to form an oxygen molecule, which is freed and enters the atmosphere.

Life is thus pushing in two opposing directions. On the one hand, animals (and plants, too) are obtaining energy for life by combining carbohydrates (and other organic foodstuffs) with oxygen to form carbon dioxide, water and energy. Green plants, on the other hand, do precisely the reverse in the presence of sunlight. They combine carbon dioxide, water and energy to make carbohydrates (and other organic foodstuffs), liberating oxygen.

The two pushes balance. The oxygen of the atmosphere never gets used up; neither does the carbon dioxide. The net result is just that, thanks to the green plant, the energy of sunlight is changed to the chemical energy that runs living tissue.

Ideally, the plant need only make enough carbohydrate for its immediate needs, as, for instance, a man might consider that he need only earn enough money to take care of immediate expenses. However, this is obviously risky business.

The plant would want to make more carbohydrate than it requires at the moment, if only to last it through the night when, in the absence of sunlight, it must consume carbohydrate to power its life processes without, temporarily, the ability to make more. So plants contain stores of carbohydrate within their tissues over and above the quantity needed for immediate use. Similarly, a man will, if he can, accumulate a bank account to take care of periods of unemployment.

Under certain conditions, the plant will need to store a considerable quantity of food. Seeds must grow for quite a while before a seedling develops green leaves which can put chlorophyll to work. To survive until that time, it must live on the energy obtained by the breakdown of carbohydrate stored in the seeds, in bulbs or in tubers.

It is these carbohydrate stores that form the chief staples of the human diet. We eat seeds like peas and beans. We make flour and bread out of the seeds of wheat, corn and other grains. We eat potatoes, yams and carrots.

Plants, in storing these energy reserves for the next generation (and, unwittingly, for us) may do so without regard for bulk and weight, since plants do not move around. For that reason, the reserves are usually in the form of starch which, although bulky, is easy to handle.

Animals must also store a food reserve. They cannot make their own at any time, but must depend upon any opportunities that may occur for stealing the food stores of plants or of other animals that have themselves survived by stealing the food stores of plants. The interval between meals is therefore irregular and may be long. All the more reason to put away a good reserve supply of energy stores during the good times for use in the lean times.

This is just what I have described as happening when the liver stores glycogen for use between meals.

However, there is a catch here. Glycogen is a kind of starch and is bulky. Some may be stored for immediate use, perhaps half a pound, but that's all. Animals move about and, in many cases, depend upon their agility to stay alive. To keep the agility high, they must keep the weight and bulk of the energy stores low, and yet they want enough of a reserve supply to give them a decent margin of safety.

The solution is to find the most concentrated type of foodstuff, something which, gram for gram, will yield the most energy.

The answer lies in the elimination of oxygen. Ordinary carbohydrate contains about one oxygen atom for every one carbon atom and two hydrogen atoms. Now in breaking down carbohydrate, it is the combining of hydrogen atoms with oxygen atoms from the atmosphere that counts. It is by virtue of that particular process that energy is produced. However, since some of the hydrogen atoms in carbohydrate are already combined with the oxygen atoms also present in the carbohydrate molecule, part of the chance to produce energy is lost.

It is as though we were buying half-burnt coal to heat our home. Part of our fuel would be already ashes and the ashed part would have considerable weight, require just as much work to heave into the furnace as the unashed part, and take up just as much room once in the furnace. And it would yield no heat.

Obviously, one must get rid of the ash. In the carbohydrate molecule that means getting rid of the oxygen atoms.

This brings us to a new type of foodstuff, the third and last of the three classes I mentioned at the beginning of Chapter 10—the *lipids*.

The lipids are greasy substances, which may be solid or liquid. As solids, they are called *fats*; if liquid, *oils*. The lipids are much poorer in oxygen than are the carbohydrates. To repeat what was stated at the beginning of Chapter 10, there is only one atom of oxygen for every ten atoms of carbon and twenty of hydrogen.

With all those hydrogen atoms in lipids virtually uncontaminated by oxygen, lipids are naturally more concentrated fuels than are carbohydrates. Lipids represent coal, so to speak, that contains very little ash.

By actual measurement, 600 grams of carbohydrate (or protein), if broken down by the body to carbon dioxide and water, will yield 2,400 kilocalories of energy, enough to keep the average man going through an average day. However, 600 grams of lipid will yield, on breakdown, no less than 5,400 kilocalories, enough to keep our man fueled for 2¼ days under ordinary conditions.

To put it another way: weight for weight, lipid will yield 2¼ times as much energy as will either carbohydrate or protein. For the sake of efficiency, then, it would be useful for an animal to keep his food stores in the form of lipids, and so it does. The body of an animal (including that of a human being) contains very little carbohydrate, but may contain large quantities of lipid. (Circus fat men may carry hundreds of pounds of lipids and still only the same 8 to 12 ounces of carbohydrate all the rest of us have.)

Our lipid supply is stored, for the main part, just under the skin. This is what is referred to as *subcutaneous fat* ("subcutaneous" comes from Latin words meaning "under the skin"). Pound for pound, women have more subcutaneous fat than men do and it is distributed more evenly. Though women may find this thought unpleasant, they should cheer up. It is this more even distribution of an ample supply that accounts for their soft, smoothly rounded and, if I may say so, delightful contours.

Fat serves not only as a food store but as a protection for the body. Some of it is stored about organs like the kidney and heart, where it serves to support them and to cushion them against mechanical shock. The fat under our skin makes us more resilient and pads us out, so that we feel the buffeting of the world less. Fat is also a poor conductor of heat, so that we are protected against the cold of winter.

It is only in excess that fat becomes dangerous. Unfortunately, the body has established no limit to the amount of fat that can be stored and it is easy to lay by enough to make ourselves shapeless and so weighted down that our mobility is interfered with. More seriously, the working parts of the body, particularly the circulatory system, groan under the weight of unnecessary fat, and give out early in life.

Once lipid is established as a food store, you may wonder why we need glycogen at all. Why not run the body on lipid only?

Unfortunately, this is impracticable. Lipid is indeed a more concentrated foodstuff due to its lack of oxygen, but it is also one that is insoluble in water due to that same lack. In fact, lipids are the classic example of a material that is insoluble in water, if you consider the well-known proverb: Oil and water do not mix.

This insolubility is a convenience in one way, since it enables the body to store lipid here and there without its going into solution and interfering with the workings of the body. I have mentioned this same convenience earlier in connection with glycogen. However, converting glycogen into soluble glucose is easy, while getting some lipid into soluble form so that it may enter the blood stream and be shipped about to various parts of the body is a comparatively complicated job.

The body compromises, then, by maintaining two types of food stores: a small store of glycogen for quick use; and a larger store of lipid for slower mobilization.

A ready analogy suggests itself in the fact that it is usual to keep a small supply of cash in the house for petty transactions that crop up, and, let us hope, a much larger sum of money in the bank, where it is not so easy to get hold of on the spur of the moment, but which, given a little time, can be retrieved and put to use.

So it comes about that the liquid portion of the body is a *two-phase system*. That is, it is made up of two different liquids which do not mix, and between which there is a definite boundary. You can make such a system for yourself by adding olive oil to water. If you do so, you will observe the olive oil floating on top of the water. There will clearly be two separate liquids with a definite *phase boundary* between.

If the olive oil and water mixture is placed in a stoppered container and strongly shaken, the two phases will be mechanically mixed into a froth of olive oil bubbles and water bubbles. Let it stand, though, and the olive oil bubbles will join, the water bubbles will join, and in the end all will be as at the beginning. There will be olive oil above, water below and a phase boundary between.

Now the liquid portion of the body is made up of an *aqueous phase* and a *lipid phase*. The aqueous phase contains not only water (the Latin word for "water" is *aqua*) but also substances which are soluble in water, such as the various inorganic ions, sugar, many proteins and so on. The lipid phase contains not only fat, but also substances which are soluble in fat, such as steroids and certain vitamins.

Nevertheless, although these two phases are separate, the body is a single functioning unit and it must have ways of bringing the two together, when necessary. One of the times when it is necessary is during digestion.

Fat is a valuable portion of our diet. Since it is a concentrated energy store, fatty foods like butter, bacon or fried food generally, have more kilocalories per gram than non-fatty foods, such as lean meat, skim milk or even potatoes. To those of us who are overweight (including the author, alas) this is no recommendation for fatty foods. For people who are underweight or people who live in cold climates or who regularly engage in hard physical labor, it is. (Besides a certain quantity of fat makes for tastier food and greater ease of cooking.)

Yet when fat is eaten, how is the body to digest it? The digestive fluids are definitely part of the aqueous phase. They are mostly water and the digestive enzymes, which dissolve freely in water, will not dissolve in fat. (In general, what will dissolve in the aqueous phase will not dissolve in the lipid phase, and vice versa.)

As far as carbohydrates and proteins are concerned, this presents no problem. Carbohydrates and proteins will either dissolve in water or be thoroughly wet by it. In either case, the enzyme molecules can get close to the carbohydrate or protein molecules and bring about their digestive breakdown.

Fat, however, is part of the lipid phase. It will not mix with the watery digestive fluid. It forms largish globules even if churned up with the digestive fluid. Except for those fat molecules which happen to be right at the surface of the globules, the enzymes have nothing they can work on.

Some sort of mediator, or go-between, is needed; something that will reconcile the two phases. And that mediator exists.

All molecules are made up of atoms which are, in turn, made up of still smaller particles. Some of these still smaller, *sub-atomic particles* carry electric charges. There are two types of such charges, arbitrarily called "positive" and "negative."

In some molecules, the distribution of these electrically charged particles is asymmetric. There is an accumulation of a slight excess of positive charge at one end of the molecule and an accumulation of an equally slight excess of negative charge at the other. Such a molecule has a positive and a negative pole, in other words, and is therefore called a *polar molecule*. The water molecule is the most familiar example of this.

Other molecules exist in which the positive and negative charges are symmetrically distributed. There is no point in the molecule where one or the other clearly predominates, so there are no electrical poles. These are *non-polar molecules* and lipid molecules are the most familiar examples.

In general, polar molecules of different types tend to mix easily. Thus water and ethyl alcohol, both possessing polar molecules, intermix freely. Non-polar molecules of different types also tend to mix freely, so that carbon tetrachloride (a common dry-cleaning fluid) will easily dissolve lipids.

Polar molecules and non-polar molecules, however, do not mix easily.

And now consider this: what if there should be a molecule with two ends of different chemical composition; with one end possessing a symmetrical distribution of electrical charge and the other an asymmetric distribution? One end would be non-polar, while the other end would be polar.

Such a molecule would be torn in two directions. The polar part would mix easily with water; the non-polar part with lipid. If such molecules were introduced into a two-phase system consisting of water and lipid, they would get into the phase boundary so that the polar half could stick into the water, the non-polar into the lipid.

Imagine such a mixture being shaken. The two phases would break up into bubbles. Each bubble, whether of water or lipid, would be surrounded by a phase boundary into which our double-action molecule would quickly make its way.

Once the shaking is done, the various bubbles might be expected to join and the two phases separate out; and so they would, if the double-action molecules were absent. As it is, however, two bubbles cannot join unless they first force the double-action molecules out of the phase boundaries, and this takes energy.

The double-action molecules thus tend to prevent reunion of the bubbles. In fact, every further motion breaks up the bubbles into still smaller bubbles, which then cannot reunite. The process continues with the bubbles becoming smaller and smaller until the two phases are so thoroughly and intimately mixed as to present almost a single phase.

Such an intimately mixed two-phase system is called an *emulsion* and the most familiar example is homogenized milk, in which the lipid globules have been made so small that they no longer coalesce and separate out as a layer of cream. Instead of a two-phase system, the milk has become, for all practical purposes, a one-phase system.

Molecules that accelerate the emulsification process are called *emulsifiers* and an example is soap. Dirt is hardest to wash away when it is mixed with grease or fat. Soap emulsifies the grease or fat and then dirt washes off more easily.

This general principle applies in the body. Once the food enters the small intestine, it is drenched in pancreatic juice and in the *bile,* a fluid produced by the liver. The pancreatic juice contains an enzyme called *pancreatic lipase,* which can break down lipid molecules rapidly, if it can get at them.

Fortunately, the bile, although it contains no enzymes at all, does contain molecules of *bile acids* and *bile salts,* which are double-action molecules of the type I've described. They coat the boundaries between the lipid globules of the food and the water of the digestive fluids. As the muscular action of the walls of the intestine breaks up the globules, the bile salts get into the new boundaries that are formed and prevent reunion.

The liquid is quickly emulsified in this way. The pancreatic lipase surrounds the microscopic droplets that result. It can get at the lipid molecules, which are then broken down and absorbed.

A lipid molecule, under the influence of lipase, breaks up into four parts. Three of these are molecules made up of long chains of carbon atoms to which hydrogen atoms are attached; in general, two hydrogen atoms to each carbon. The carbon atom at one end of the chain has a pair of oxygen atoms plus a hydrogen atom attached, and this makes up a carboxyl group.

The carboxyl group lends weakly acid properties to the long molecule, which, in addition, shares certain properties with the lipid molecule from which it has been obtained. That is, it has a greasy feel and will leave a translucent "grease spot" on paper. The combination of fatty properties and acid properties results in these substances being termed *fatty acids*.

The fourth part of the lipid molecule is *glycerol*. It consists of a small molecule with only a three-carbon chain. To each of these carbons is attached a hydroxyl group (an oxygen atom and hydrogen atom combination). A fatty acid can be attached to a glycerol molecule by a combination of the carboxyl group of the former with one of the hydroxyl groups of the latter. A second and third fatty acid can be combined with the second and third hydroxyl groups of the glycerol.

In this way, a *glyceride* is formed, consisting, so to speak, of three long carbon chains tied up by a short cross-piece at one end. Such a molecule consists entirely of carbon and hydrogen atoms except at the points where fatty acid has been hooked up with the glycerol. At each of those points, two oxygen atoms exist; six altogether in the molecule.

Glyceride molecules differ in the exact nature of the fatty acid portion of the molecules. Individual fatty acids may differ, for instance, in the length of the carbon chain. Thus, there is a common fatty acid containing a 16-carbon chain, which is called *palmitic acid*. Another one, with an 18-carbon chain, is *stearic acid*.

Fatty acids may also differ in the number of hydrogen atoms present in the molecule. Palmitic acid and stearic acid are holding all the hydrogen atoms they can. They are examples of *saturated fatty acids* (saturated with hydrogen, that is).

One common fatty acid has an 18-carbon chain like that of stearic acid, but is missing a pair of hydrogen atoms in the very center of the chain. It is *oleic acid* and is an example of an *unsaturated fatty acid. Linoleic acid* also has an 18-carbon chain, but is missing two pairs of hydrogen atoms.

The various fatty acids can combine with glycerol in any combination. A particular glyceride may contain a palmitic acid and two oleic acids, or an oleic acid, a stearic acid and a linoleic acid, or three palmitic acids. They may contain any of a dozen or more less common varieties of fatty acids. Lipids are made up of a mixture of hundreds of different glyceride molecules.

Unsaturated fatty acids have lower melting points than do saturated fatty acids. Lipids with molecules containing a relatively large number of such unsaturated fatty acids, therefore, have lower melting points than those which do not. The unsaturated lipids are liquid at room temperature (oils); the more saturated ones are solid at room temperature (fats).

In a living organism, lipids must be liquid if they are to be handled properly. Plants and cold-blooded animals, which may be exposed to fairly low temperatures, keep their lipids quite unsaturated so they won't freeze. (That is why cod-liver oil and cotton-seed oil are liquid even on a cold day.)

Warm-blooded creatures can allow their lipids to be more saturated, since they need be liquid only at blood heat. For this reason butter, lard and tallow are solid at room temperature but will melt easily if warmed.

By mixing gaseous hydrogen with a molecule of oil under the proper conditions, hydrogen atoms are added to those places in the molecule where they are missing. The unsaturated fatty acids become saturated; oils become fats. In this way, relatively cheap vegetable oils, which may themselves be unfit for kitchen use, can be converted to margarine and vegetable shortenings.

In general, the mammalian body, including our own, can do this sort of thing, too. It can convert oleic acid to stearic acid and vice versa. Therefore, it doesn't matter whether our diets include a large quantity of either saturated or unsaturated fatty acid. We can always adjust it to suit our needs.

There is one exception, though. Although our bodies can withdraw one pair of hydrogen atoms from stearic acid to make oleic acid, they cannot, for some reason, withdraw a second pair to form linoleic acid. If linoleic acid is not present in our diet, then, we cannot make our own, and the result is a disorder of which the visible symptom is a skin-inflammation and eczema. Linoleic acid is an example of a *dietarily-essential fatty acid*. (This is not as serious a dietary problem as that of the essential amino acids, because actually almost any diet would have enough linoleic acid in it for our needs.)

Actually, linoleic acid seems to be necessary for us not in itself but because it can be converted into another acid (much less common), which is called *arachidonic acid*. This latter has a molecule made up of a 20-carbon chain with no less than four pairs of hydrogen atoms missing. Arachidonic acid occurs particularly in the adrenal glands, but what its function is, why it should be necessary to our body chemistry, is as yet not known. No one can even think up a plausible guess as yet.

After digestion, the glycerol and fatty acids are absorbed through the walls of the small intestine. It is possible that absorption takes place even without complete digestion; that glycerol molecules, to which one or even two fatty acids are still hanging on, may be absorbed.

In any case, once in the cells of the small intestine wall, the glycerides are reformed and enter the blood circulation as complete molecules. For the most part, though, they do not enter the blood directly.

In each villus of the small intestine there is not only a capillary, but also a tiny lymphatic vessel. Whereas the products of the digestion of carbohydrate and protein enter the capillary as glucose or amino acids, respectively, most of the products of lipid digestion and absorption enter the lymphatic.

The lymph contained in the lymphatic turns white with the influx of small globules of lipid, such white lymph being called *chyle.* In fact, because of the resulting milky appearance of the chyle, these particular lymphatics are called *lacteals,* from the Latin word for "milk."

The fat globules drift through the lymphatic system and eventually enter the blood circulation proper. On the way, though, they are in contact with the various body cells and much of the lipid molecules are absorbed.

Such lipid as enters the capillaries of the villi directly is carried to the liver. There the various fatty acids are adjusted by lengthening or shortening the chain and by removing or adding hydrogen atoms until the human pattern of lipids is attained.

Once fat is absorbed by the cells, it can be broken down for energy (if so desired) by means of a series of controlled reactions that make up the *fatty acid oxidation cycle.* By means of this cycle, carbon atoms are split off the fatty acid chain two at a time and each "two-carbon fragment" is (or can be) broken down to carbon dioxide, water and energy.

The cycle can also run backward, which is useful since carbohydrate can also be broken down to the same two-carbon fragment. Thus, if too much glucose is being absorbed for storage as glycogen, it can always be broken up into two-carbon fragments, which can be run backward up the fatty acid oxidation cycle until eight or nine of them are combined into fatty acids. The fatty acids can then be hooked on to glycerol molecules (easily formed by the body in a number of ways) and stored away as lipid.

Now the breakdown of two-carbon fragments to carbon

dioxide and water depends on the formation of certain intermediate compounds, chiefly one called *oxaloacetic acid*. This compound is easily formed in the process of carbohydrate breakdown, but not in the process of lipid breakdown.

If, then, for some reason, two-carbon fragments are being formed only from lipids and not from carbohydrates, there is trouble. Oxaloacetic acid can be formed by alternative routes, but not rapidly enough in the absence of carbohydrate breakdown, and the two-carbon fragments aren't handled as rapidly as they are being formed.

There is a "log-jam," so to speak, and some of the two-carbon fragments, while waiting around, combine in pairs to form a four-carbon compound called *acetoacetic acid*. The acetoacetic acid, also hanging around, can add two hydrogen atoms to form *betahydroxybutyric acid* or can lose a molecule of carbon dioxide to form *acetone*. These three molecules together are usually referred to as *ketone bodies*.

Suppose, for instance, you were fasting. Your glycogen stores would be used up during the first day. After that, you would start living on your lipid stores. This works. You can manufacture enough glucose (by stripping lipid molecules to two-carbon fragments and combining them three at a time) to keep the blood level at the proper point.

However, because you are not breaking down carbohydrate, you are accumulating ketone bodies (*starvation ketosis*). These show up in the blood (*ketonemia*) and spill over into the urine (*ketonuria*).

This is not a particularly serious condition and disappears quickly once you eat food that contains a reasonable quantity of starch or sugar. (Of course, if your diet is high in fat and low in carbohydrate, ketosis continues. In fact, such a diet is termed *ketogenic;* that is, "giving birth to ketosis.")

A more serious form of ketosis is that which arises when the body is incapable of breaking down carbohydrate, as in diabetes. In the untreated diabetic, ketone bodies accumulate (*diabetic ketosis*) to a considerably greater extent than in a normal fasting person. They accumulate in the blood faster than the kidneys can get rid of them and, since they are distinctly acid, a *diabetic acidosis* results which eventually leads to coma and death.

The two-phase system of lipid and water is adequately

handled, as I have described, in the small intestine itself, with the help of the bile salts. Once lipids are within the blood stream and in the cells, however, they form a separate phase again. How are these water-spurning lipids carried across membranes into the cell? How are they transported through the bloom stream? How do the essentially aqueous enzymes get at them within the cell to break them down?

The body manages all this by making use of another type of double-action compound, strongly resembling the glycerides themselves in some cases.

The glycerides I have already discussed, made up of combinations of glycerol and fatty acids only, are *simple lipids*. But imagine molecules made up of glycerol to which two fatty acids only are attached. The third hydroxyl group of glycerol is attached to a completely different type of atom combination containing oxygen, nitrogen and phosphorous atoms (all of which make for electrical polarity when present in a molecule). Because of the presence of the phosphorous atom, these are usually referred to as *phospholipids* or *phosphatides*.

Phospholipids are double-action molecules. The fatty acid portion is soluble in the lipid phase, the phosphorus-containing portion is soluble in the aqueous phase. This makes possible an interesting theory concerning the behavior of cell membranes. (It's only a theory I happen to like. The study of cell membrane action is still, alas, in its infancy, and I can't speak with any kind of assurance.)

Certainly, though, there are both phospholipids and proteins present in membranes. So much seems sure. Now the phosphorus-containing end of the phospholipids, being aqueous phase material, probably sticks firmly to the proteins (which are also aqueous phase), leaving the fatty acid portion of the phospholipids swinging free, so to speak.

Thus, the cell membrane is made up of a continuous substance with, perhaps, aqueous phase "patches" through which aqueous phase materials can pass through and lipid phase "patches" through which lipid phase substances can pass through.

If this were so, it might also explain the workings of the various hormones. Some of the hormones, such as insulin and those manufactured by the pituitary gland are protein in nature and form part of the aqueous phase. Others, like the sex hormones and those formed by the adrenal cortex, form part of the lipid phase. In either case, if their molecules are layered on to cell membranes, they might alter the permeability by obscuring some patches and reinforcing others, making it easier for aqueous phase materials to get through and harder for lipid phase materials or vice versa. By shifting the nature of the raw material with which the cell can work, the hormones can alter the workings and induce far-reaching results.

Within the cell, phospholipid is also in evidence, particularly in small particles within the cytoplasm, which are called *mitochondria*. It is within these mitochondria that carbohydrate and lipid are broken down for energy purposes and it seems very likely to me that the phospholipid contained there is for the purpose of helping to bring aqueous-phase enzymes and lipid-phase fatty acids together.

Phospholipid, all told, makes up only 1 per cent or so of the body. However, its importance can be shown by this: the body never touches it no matter what the emergency. During an indefinite fast, the body will first use up its carbohydrate, then live on its fat stores, then start stripping its tissue protein. But even down to the point of final death, the phospholipids remain intact, even though their energy content, gram for gram, is higher than that of carbohydrate or protein. Apparently, to burn up even a small portion of the phospholipids will so derange the bodily workings as to result in death anyway, so why bother.

I have showed (or theorized) how phospholipids might help lipid phase materials across cell membranes and how they might aid in the handling of those same materials within the cell. What about the transport of lipid phase materials by the blood stream, however?

At the close of the previous chapter, I stressed the importance of the plasma proteins as a means of carrying vitamins, hormones and other materials from one point of the body to another. But the plasma proteins are aqueous phase substances; they have to be to remain soluble in the plasma. How, then, can they transport lipid-phase hormones or vitamins?

Just as phospholipids and proteins can combine by way of the phosphorus-containing group in the phospholipid molecule to form a cell membrane of two-phase properties, so they can combine in the same manner in blood to form a double-action molecule. In combination, phospholipid and plasma protein form *lipoproteins*.

Lipid phase materials join freely with the lipid portion of the lipoprotein and can be carried along without trouble. The protein portion keeps the whole freely soluble in the aqueous blood plasma.

In this way, the lipoproteins, which only make up 3 to 5 per cent of the plasma proteins altogether, are nevertheless an essential part of the blood's transport scheme. In fact, in the last twenty years, scientists have suddenly turned a fascinated and somewhat horrified gaze on these compounds, which earlier had been little known and less regarded.

To explain why, I must first begin by saying that one important lipid phase material is *cholesterol*. The molecule of this compound is made up of a four-ring system of carbon atoms, loaded with hydrogen atoms at all points but one, and there a single hydroxyl group is attached. By way of this hydroxyl group, the cholesterol may be hooked on to one fatty acid, or it may not be.

There is more than 200 grams of cholesterol in the body. It is partly needed as a raw material for the formation of the sex hormones and the cortical hormones (which are similar to cholesterol in molecular structure). Very little is needed for that, though.

The major part of the cholesterol is found in cell membranes and, most particularly, in the fatty sheaths that surround nerve fibers. Because of this last, the dry matter of the brain (that is, ignoring the water content) is one-fifth cholesterol.

Why cholesterol is needed there, and why some other lipid-phase material won't do instead, no one can even begin to explain. Nevertheless, for whatever reason it may be there, it is important. It is important enough for the blood stream to be forever dragging it hither and thither, and cholesterol is one of the materials that most clogs up the lipoproteins of the plasma.

In fact, the lipoproteins may be divided into two main classes. One consists of relatively small molecules containing phosphoglycerides and only small amounts of cholesterol. These are the *alpha-liproproteins*. The rest are much larger molecules, with at least some of the additional weight resulting from the piling on of cholesterol until more than half the lipid phase portion of the molecule is made up of it. These are the *beta-lipoproteins*. ("Alpha" and "beta" are the first two letters of the Greek alphabet.)

And now here is the distressing part of the story. Even the lipoproteins do not always represent a perfect solution to the problem of transporting lipid-phase materials. There is always a tendency for some of the material to "spill off" as the blood stream careens on its way. This is more likely to happen in men than in women, though we don't know why; and in some men more than others; again we don't know why.

But the material which is most likely to spill off the lipoprotein carrier is cholesterol, perhaps because of its presence in comparatively high quantity. Once it spills off, the aqueous phase plasma cannot drag it along and the cholesterol settles instead onto the inner membranes of the blood vessels (where it may find phospholipid to hang on to). This happens, generally, in the arteries, perhaps because there the blood stream is at its swiftest and cholesterol is most easily torn off its carrier.

Once cholesterol begins clogging up the inner surface of an artery, it narrows the bore and thus increases the blood pressure at that point. Furthermore, it reduces the elasticity of the arterial wall so that there is an increased danger of a break under the additional stress. Furthermore, the internal surface becomes rough and ragged, offering opportunities for blood clots (which I will discuss in the last chapter) to form and perhaps block off a particular vessel entirely. This last is called *thrombosis*.

When thrombosis occurs in the coronary arteries that feed the heart, the result is what is commonly known as a "heart attack." In the small arteries of the brain, a stopped blood vessel may mean the starvation of a patch of brain with a consequent "paralytic stroke." Either way, death is near.

The condition of cholesterol settling out on the inner walls of the arteries is known as *atherosclerosis*. Now that infectious diseases have been brought under such good control by means of vaccination, community hygiene and antibiotics, atherosclerosis has become the number one killer of mankind (more so than womankind) in the western world.

Nothing can be done about atherosclerosis once it has messed up the arteries, but it would be useful if there were some way in which we could tell in advance who is more likely to suffer from atherosclerosis some day and who is less likely. The first could take care of himself with that knowledge in mind and live the longer for it. He can, for instance, taper off on strenuous exercise earlier in life than the second would need to.

For instance, since it is the beta-lipoproteins that carry the lion's share of the cholesterol, perhaps a blood stream with more than its share of beta-lipoprotein is to be suspect. This may be so. At least, it has been reported that the blood of diabetics (who are known to be more prone to atherosclerosis than are non-diabetics) is particularly high in beta-lipoprotein as compared with that of normal human beings.

Therefore, after World War II, when peace-time research could absorb a larger share of the attention of scientists, ways and means for a more detailed probing of the lipoproteins was looked for. An answer came about as follows:

Ordinarily, protein molecules, though somewhat denser than water, do not settle out of water as particles of sand (also denser than water) would. The protein molecules are being pulled down by gravity, but they are being kept "stirred up" and in solution by the random collisions of water molecules with the protein molecules. Sand particles are also being bombarded by water molecules, but they are so large that they are scarcely affected by the tiny collisions. The much smaller protein molecules are affected, on the other hand.

We could allow the protein molecules to settle out if we slowed down the water molecules, but that could only be done by cooling the solution, which would then freeze long before the molecules had been made sufficiently slow.

An alternative is to increase the gravitational pull on the protein molecules. We can't increase gravity itself, but we can introduce a force which behaves like gravity and which we can increase. If we put a protein solution in a small container and whirl it round and round rapidly, there is a *centrifugal force* pressing everything in the container in the direction away from the center of rotation. The faster the spin, the greater the force.

In the 1930's, the Swedish scientist, T. Svedberg, designed a centrifuge that could spin so rapidly as to create a centrifugal force hundreds of thousands of times, even millions of times, as intense as ordinary gravity. Such a device is an *ultracentri-*

fuge. (The word "centrifuge" for such a spinning device comes from Latin words meaning "fleeing from the center.")

In the ultracentrifuge, the protein molecules start drifting through the water, away from the center of rotation. They are *sedimenting* out.

The rate of sedimentation for a particular protein molecule depends upon both its size and shape. The behavior of a protein in an ultracentrifuge offers one method for determining the size of its molecule for that reason.

The sedimentation rate is measured in units called *svedbergs,* in honor of the inventer of the ultracentrifuge and is usually abbreviated s_{20}. (The "20" signifies that the temperature of the solution being centrifuged is kept at 20° C.)

Now lipoproteins behave just as do ordinary proteins when ultracentrifuged—with one important difference. Lipids, generally, are only 75 to 80 per cent as dense as water. The low density of the lipid portion of a lipoprotein more than makes up for the slightly high density of the protein portion. The lipoprotein as a whole is therefore lighter than water; and the more lipid there is in proportion to protein in the lipoprotein, the lighter it is.

Lipoproteins, under the influence of ultracentrifugal spin, therefore, move not away, but toward the center of rotation. The rate at which the lipoproteins move toward the center of rotation can be measured in negative svedbergs or, as they are usually called, *svedbergs of flotation,* abbreviated s_f.

The lipoproteins of plasma have been studied in this fashion and have been divided into groups depending on the rate at which they move in the ultracentrifuge. The fraction moving most slowly (s_f 3-8) varies from one individual to another, but remains constant for any one individual. The amount you have of that fraction will not change with your diet or state of health.

It is the s_f 12-20 group that is receiving the major attention. That is the one that seems to be connected with atherosclerosis. If that fraction is high in an individual, his chances for suffering from the disease go up.

The next question is: can anything be done to keep that fraction low? Is there any dietary key? It would seem that we ought to keep away from cholesterol since the fraction is high in cholesterol and it is cholesterol that does the major share of damage to the artery linings. Unfortunately, the body can make cholesterol with supreme ease, and even on a low-cholesterol diet (i.e. one which eliminates butter, eggs and animal fat generally) it is possible to have a high s_f 12-20 fraction. Nor is it certain that high cholesterol in the diet will increase the fraction.

There is no answer just yet. At least, though, it seems that scientists are looking in the right direction, so we'll see what the next few years will bring.

Chapter 13

Warding Off the Outer Peril

IT IS POSSIBLE to cause protein molecules to settle out of solution by other means than the forcible pulling described at the end of the previous chapter. The same result can be achieved by making them less soluble in water. If the water, for one reason or another, cannot maintain a distance among the individual protein molecules, these will clump together and settle out as fine crystals or as fibrous clumps or as gelatinous masses, depending on the particular protein involved.

One way of making it impossible for the water to keep the protein molecules apart is to give the water something else to do. (You might boil the water away, but the heat will destroy the protein.) For instance, a new substance is dissolved in the water. Water molecules will tend to surround the ions or molecules of this newly added substance and there will be fewer water molecules available to surround the protein molecules.

A time-honored substance used in this way is *ammonium sulfate* which, in chemical parlance, is an example of an "excessively soluble" salt. (A *salt* is any one of a group of compounds which splits up into ions on solution and which can be formed by reacting an acid and a base. Ordinary table salt is an example and gave its name to the group as a whole.) Thus, 100 grams of water at room temperature will dissolve about 80 grams of ammonium sulfate.

The ammonium sulfate is added to the protein solution in

installments. It is quite likely that after each installment, some protein will (perhaps slowly) precipitate. If there is more than one variety of protein present, one variety, after all, may well be less soluble than the others. This less soluble variety will then precipitate out when a relatively small amount of ammonium sulfate has been added; an amount that is as yet insufficient to bring about the precipitation of the more soluble varieties.

The use of ammonium sulfate (or other salts) to precipitate proteins from solution is called *salting out*. Salting out in installments to divide the proteins in solution into the less soluble and more soluble fractions is called *salt fractionation*.

Shortly after World War I it was found that, by salt fractionation, two broad groups of plasma proteins could be recognized. One part precipitated when the plasma was only holding half the ammonium sulfate it could hold; (it was then *half-saturated*). This was the *plasma globulin*. If the precipitated globulin were filtered off and additional ammonium sulfate added to the clear solution until it held all the ammonium sulfate it could hold (it was then *saturated*), the remaining protein precipitated. This was the *plasma albumin*.

In every 100 ml. of blood plasma, there are about 6 grams of plasma proteins. Of these, about 2½ grams are plasma globulin and about 3½ grams are plasma albumin.

The plasma albumin molecules are the smaller. They are, on the average, about 69,000 in molecular weight, or just a trifle heavier than the hemoglobin molecule. The plasma globulin molecules vary considerably in size but 200,000 is a conservative estimate of the average molecular weight.

Since the plasma globulin molecule averages three times the size of the plasma albumin molecule, it follows that one gram of plasma albumin contains three times as many molecules as does one gram of plasma globulin. Furthermore, since albumin outweighs globulin by 3½ to 2½ in the blood plasma, it follows that about four out of every five plasma protein molecules are albumin.

Now the osmotic pressure (which I described in Chapter 10) depends upon the number of protein molecules present in the plasma and not (within limits) upon the actual weight of the individual molecule. It also follows, therefore, that plasma albumin is responsible for about 80 per cent of the entire osmotic pressure effect. The albumin is dried, powdered and placed in sealed containers ready for use after water and minerals are added.

Plasma albumin is probably also responsible for the major portion of the plasma protein's nutritional value and action as transport vehicle for smaller molecules. It would be a mistake, though, to underestimate the importance of the globulin fraction. That has certain values of its own.

Actually, salting out by ammonium sulfate is a crude method of separation, and better methods have since been devised for picking apart the plasma proteins.

The two chief methods have both been mentioned before. One is Cohn's alcohol-fractionation method, which I talked about in connection with plasma expanders at the end of Chapter 11. The second is electrophoresis, which I talked about in connection with abnormal hemoglobins at the beginning of Chapter 7.

The electrophoresis of plasma proteins, in particular, is now a very common procedure. When the plasma proteins are pulled apart as a result of their different rates of motion in an electric field, the most rapidly moving (under the usual conditions) turns out to be the plasma albumin. It moves almost in one piece.

The plasma globulins, however, are made up of molecules so diverse that under the pull of the electric current the response is sufficiently different to result in separation into subgroups. The plasma globulins fall into three chief subgroups, which are termed *alpha-globulins, beta globulins* and *gamma-globulins,* the alpha variety being the fastest moving, beta slower and gamma slowest. (Alpha, beta and gamma are the first three leters of the Greek alphabet.)

Each of these groups is itself made up of diverse molecules and a particularly detailed electrophoresis may show the alpha and beta groups themselves dividing in two. It is therefore possible to speak of an $alpha_1$-globulin and an $alpha_2$-globulin.

It is, however, the gamma-globulin fraction which has received the lion's share of attention. In every 100 milliliters of plasma there is 0.66 grams of gamma-globulin, so that this fraction makes up only 11 per cent of the weight of plasma proteins as a whole. Nevertheless, it has a peculiar importance.

For instance, during many types of infections, the quantity of gamma-globulins in the blood increases markedly. This was noticed, actually, in the years before electrophoresis had given a basis for dividing up the globulins in the alpha, beta, gamma system.

When the only division was into albumin and globulin, people spoke of an *A/G ratio,* that is, the ratio of the weights of albumin and globulin in the blood. For instance, if 100 ml. of normal blood plasma contained 3½ grams of albumin and 2½ grams of globulin, then the normal A/G ratio is 3½/2½ or 1.4.

In a variety of infections, this value went down. Now we know this is because the gamma-globulin fraction goes up. If it goes up enough to cause the globulin in general to rise to 3 grams per 100 ml. of blood plasma then the A/G ratio becomes 3½ or 1.17.

In the early days of plasma fractionation, it was hoped that the A/G ratio would be a good diagnostic aid. Unfortunately, so many different things could raise the globulin level (or lower the albumin level, which is the same thing as far as A/G ratio is concerned) that it was useless.

In later years, when electrophoresis became common, hopes rose again on a new basis. Perphaps the exact manner in which blood plasma divided up into albumin and the various globulins would differ in sick people from that in healthy people. Perhaps each variety of sickness might give its own "electrophoretic pattern." The blood might, in other words, offer a kind of "fingerprint" for health and disease.

That hope was also blasted. In certain conditions, changes can be seen (usually an increase in gamma-globulins), but on the whole the blood maintains its normal characteristics even in sickness.

But to get back to the gamma-globulins.

Another hint at the importance of this fraction of the plasma proteins lies in the history of those very few children (always male, incidentally), who are so unfortunate as to be born without the ability of manufacturing gamma-globulins. (This condition is called *agammaglobulinemia.*) Such children have frequent severe bacterial infections and, without care, would die at an early age. With care, in this modern age of antibiotics, the children can be kept alive, but the antibiotics must be kept ready at all times.

Obviously, the gamma-globulins have something to do with

the body's defense against infection. They include those protein molecules called "antibodies," so it becomes time to consider antibodies and infection generally for a while.

Life is a completely pitiless competition. Animals eat each other or fall upon the comparatively helpless plant world. And green plants, which make their own food and which don't prey directly on their fellows, are yet far from innocent. They compete with no holds barred for sun and water. The dandelion may not eat grass, but it kills grass just the same.

Any creature, plant or animal, that avoids hungry enemies long enough to die a "natural" death (one brought about by some physical or chemical failure in the body mechanism) is then devoured to the last scrap by scavengers and bacteria.

The micro-organisms are the great eaters of the world of life, for what escapes all else will not escape them. For that matter, they do not require that an organism be dead to serve as food. Bacteria live within our tissues scavenging a living at our expense. Viruses live within our cells. This practice of living at the expense of an organism not yet dead is called *parasitism*.

It sounds disgusting and unfair, but it is apparently a very workable state of affairs since there are animals and plants of all types (and not merely micro-organisms) that have taken to a parasitic way of life. In a way, we ourselves can't afford to be too sanctimonious in our disapproval of it, since we are in a sense parasitic on herds of cattle and fields of grain. No doubt, if cattle and grain could think about it, they would consider us disgusting and unfair.

But, fair or not, since there are micro-organisms which are perfectly willing to make a meal out of us as we stand, we must have defenses against them. Otherwise—considering that they surround us everywhere, that they multiply with incredible speed and are ready to begin that multiplication at our expense at any time—we are dead men.

Our first line of defense is a wall; the wall of our skin. It is quite germ-proof and while it is intact, we are usually safe. (Only "usually." Some parasitic worms have learnt the trick of boring through intact skin. Children who habitually walk barefoot in some sections of this country run the risk of developing hookworm. In countries like Egypt, peasants who work barefoot in shallow water often pick up another kind of parasitic worm and develop schistosomiasis.)

There are chinks in the armor, though. The mucus membranes about our eyes and in our nose, mouth and throat are thinner than skin and less effective as barriers. The frequent infections we all suffer in the nose and throat area are proof enough of that. Then, too, the skin is all too often broken by accident and even a small scratch can, if the breaks are all bad, lead to a germ invasion that can be fatal.

Obviously, then, while the skin is an excellent barrier, we can't trust to it entirely. A second line of defense, effective against micro-organisms that have gotten past the skin, is necessary. This second line of defense is in the blood.

Back in Chapter 3, I listed three types of formed elements: erythrocytes, leukocytes and thrombocytes. I went on, however, to talk only about the erythrocytes, and neither of the other two has been mentioned since. Now it is time to mention the leukocyte, since that is the second line of defense against infection.

Leukocyte is a word that is derived from Greek words meaning *white cell* and that, indeed, is a common alternative name for them. They are the ordinary color of cells and are called "white" in distinction to the red cells. Unlike the red cells, the white cells are true cells of normal size and possessing a nucleus.

There are many fewer white cells than there are red; only about 7,000 of the former for every cubic millimeter of blood as compared with 4 to 5 million of the latter, so that the white cells are outnumbered 650 to 1. Even 7,000 per cubic millimeter adds up to a tidy number taken over the entire body, however; about 75,000,000,000 white cells, all told, in the average man.

The leukocytes may be divided into a number of varieties, differing among themselves in size and in the shape of the nucleus. One kind, the *polymorphonuclear leukocyte*, makes up about three fifths of all the white cells. Like the red cells, these are formed in the bone marrow. The preliminary stages are the *myeloblasts* and *myelocytes*. The polymorphonuclear leukocytes are particularly interesting in that they have ameboid motion. That is, they move by methods similar to that of the well-known one-celled animal, the ameba. In such a motion, the cell simply thrusts out a bulge in the direction in which it wants to travel. The cell fluid flows into the bulge, another bulge appears and so on.

This gives the leukocytes almost the appearance of independent life, as they crawl about on the walls of blood vessels and even through the walls of capillaries, squeezing between the cells that make up those walls. They would appear almost to be infesting us like germs, until we get a chance to see on whose side they are, so to speak.

The leukocyte shows its true function when it happens to meet a real germ, an invading bacterium that has gotten past the skin. When that happens, the leukocyte calmly engulfs the germ and digests it. The process is known as *phagocytosis* (from Greek words meaning "eating of cells").

When germs have invaded through a break in the skin, the blood vessels relax so that more blood can be rushed to the site. White cells are brought to the spot by the blood stream. Additional white cells in the neighborhood get to the battle scene by virtue of their own movement. All this brings about inflammation and swelling, and the unusual pressure of fluid results in pain; all due to the body's mobilization of defenses rather than to the bacterial attack itself.

The fight is often a hard one, though, and white cells are not always the eaters. If the bacteria sufficiently outnumber them, white cells are destroyed. The destroyed white cells collect at the site of infection as *pus*.

Bacteria which evade the white cells at the immediate site of infection and get into the circulation proper are filtered out at the lymph nodes (enlarged section occurring here and there along the course of the lymphatics). White cells capable of phagocytosis occur at these lymph nodes and subsidiary battles go on there. In the process the lymph nodes swell and become painful under pressure, just as the original site of infection does. It is for this reason, therefore, that one of the signs of a throat infection, for instance, is the presence of "swollen glands" at the angles of the jaw. These are the lymph nodes that happen to be nearest the site of infection.

If the white cells are viewed, picturesquely, as an army serving the body against the foreign invader, the metaphor can be carried further. An army can sometimes go out of control and prove a greater danger to those who originally used it than were the invaders against which it was employed.

It sometimes happens, for instance, that the bone marrow forming the white cells runs out of control and begins an over-production of polymorphonuclear leucocytes. Or, alternatively, the lymph node tissue gets out of hand and produces too many lymphocytes, which, next to the polymorphonuclear leucocytes, are the most common variety of white cell, making up about one fourth of the total under normal conditions. The lymphocytes are formed in the lymph nodes, which is why they are present in lymph. In either case, immature white cells crowd into the blood stream, reaching a count of 100,000 or sometimes even 1,000,000 per cubic millimeter, 15 to 150 times the normal count. The other formed elements decrease in numbers correspondingly so that there is anemia and an increased tendency to bleed. (The connection between formed elements and bleeding will be described in the next chapter.) In the end, which may come quite soon, or be delayed for years, the anemia is fatal.

This disease is *leukemia* (from Greek words meaning "white blood," really a shortened form of "too many white cells in blood"). Since leukemia is the result of uncontrolled growth; that is, the continuous formation of new and unneeded cells, it may be considered one of the diseases grouped under the name of "cancer." It is, in fact, often called "blood cancer."

The cause and cure of leukemia are as unknown as are those of other forms of cancer. A number of drugs have been tested which seem to have a beneficial effect on at least some cases, but an actual cure is not yet in sight.

Behind the white cells is still another, a third line of defense.

Faced with the invasion of objects foreign to the body, such as bacteria or viruses, those parts of the body which ordinarily produce white cells (bone marrow, lymph nodes and so on) begin to produce special proteins in addition. The lymph nodes, in particular, form the plasma globulins, perhaps through the breakup of lymphocytes.

These proteins are so designed as to combine easily with the chemical structures on the surface of the bacterial cell or of the virus.

Such a design is made possible by the number and variety of side-chains of the individual amino acids making up a protein molecule. The amino acids can be arranged so that the side-chains will just "fit" some part of the bacterial surface. The exact nature of the "fit" is not yet certainly known. It may actually be a mechanical fit; that is, the designed protein will bend inward wherever the molecules making up the surface of the bacterium bulge outward, and vice versa. If this were so, a number of atoms in the designed protein will be able to line up closely with atoms on the bacterial surface, following all the unevennesses.

Atoms that approach closely, within a distance equal to their own diameters, are attracted by weak forces (called *van der Waal's forces* after the physical chemist who first considered such forces in his theories about the behavior of gas molecules). When a number of atoms of one protein line up next to those of another, the individual van der Waal's forces mount up and become an over-all strong attractive force between the molecules. If the fit is not perfect, enough atoms remain at distances greater than their own diameter, at which point the van der Waal's forces disappear. Not enough force is left to keep the molecules together. The combination, therefore, depends very greatly on the excellence of fit.

An alternative suggestion is that the special proteins make use of electric charges. Some of the amino acid side-chains normally carry a negative electric charge, some a positive. It is then necessary to design a protein that is the reverse image of a spot on the bacterial surface. Where the bacterium carries a negative charge, the protein has a positive one and vice versa. Negative charges attract positive charges, so when the protein gets into the proper position over the spot on the bacterial surface, it combines tightly as all the positive-negative combinations add their individual bits of attraction. Again, the tightness of combination that results depends upon the excellence of the "reverse-charge" fit.

In either case, the bacterium is, in a sense, used as a mold for designing the special protein. The bacterium, virus or any molecule which stimulates such a design and acts as the mold for it is called an *antigen*. The protein formed in response to the antigen is the *antibody*.

At first, the antibodies are formed slowly, but after about six days or so, they are being turned out in quantity and are pouring into the blood stream. (It is as though an automobile factory, turning out a new model, were first working slowly, ironing out the bugs and retooling the factory, and then, when that was done, began swinging into mass production.)

The antibodies in the circulation begin to combine with the antigen as they are formed. As a result of this combination some key point on the surface of the bacterium or virus is masked, and this masking serves to hamper its activities seriously. (It is as though a pianist were to find himself suddenly and unexpectedly equipped with boxing gloves which he could not remove.)

A number of things can happen to a bacterium which finds itself joined to an antibody, all bad (for the bacterium). The bacterium may be killed outright and begin to break up. Or else it becomes "sticky" and clumps together with other bacteria in a helpless mass. Or else it simply loses its ability to fight off the white cell. In all these cases, the final result is that the bacteria find themselves helpless before the attacking white cells.

Sometimes it is not the bacterium itself that makes the trouble as much as some poisonous substance (*bacterial toxin*) which it produces. Such toxins can also act as antigens, and antibodies may be formed which will combine with them and either precipitate them out of solution or otherwise neutralize their poisonous characteristics.

Once antibodies are formed, they maintain themselves in the blood stream for an indefinite period sometimes. The gamma-globulin fraction of the plasma proteins consists mostly (perhaps even entirely) of samples of the various antibodies formed by the body. It is a collection of "battle scars," so to speak, of the body's continuing war against agents of infection. And it is because of this that biochemists are particularly interested in the gamma-globulin fraction.

It is the continuing presence of antibodies that makes for *immunity;* that is, the ability to be exposed to a disease without "catching" it. A child who has had chicken-pox, for instance, produces chicken-pox antibody in the process of recovery. Some remains with him. If there were an attempted new invasion in force on the part of the chicken-pox virus later in life, the antibodies would be ready and the virus would gain no foothold.

Such an immunity is usually a sign of the continuous presence of the antigen (bacterium or virus) in the body, in quantity sufficient to present molds for antibody formation, but not enough to make anyone sick. If the bacterium or virus were to leave us completely, the antibody would gradually be eliminated (no blood protein lives forever) and, without the stimulation of the antigen serving to produce more, our immunity would be lost.

So the presence of some germs in our body (even disease germs) is a good thing. And our immunity is a good thing, too, even for the germs themselves. For a parasite to be efficient, it should avoid killing the *host* (that is, the organism being infested by the parasite). Obviously, a dead host feeds no parasites.

The ideal situation is to have a small group of bacteria or viruses feeding quietly on the host, keeping their own numbers constant, and being so gently parasitic that the host is not even aware of their existence. They have a soft life and the host retains immunity against serious attacks. This is a mutual adaptation of host and parasite to each other.

An example of such a relationship involves the virus which causes "cold-sores." Most of us are infected with it without being aware of it. Only occasionally, when we are down with a cold or other such ailment so that our body defenses are unusually taken up, does the cold-sore virus find itself multiplying with less check than usual from the preoccupied defenses. Itchy eruptions develop about the mouth and we have a cold-sore. The adaptation isn't perfect, and on very rare occasions the cold-sore virus can be fatal, but it is nearly perfect.

Diseases which kill a large number of those they strike are those which show poor adaptation of parasite and host. It's bad for us, obviously, and its bad for the parasite. There seems to be a tendency for germ diseases to grow milder as they live with us over the centuries.

Unfortunately, there are always new diseases showing up. There has been some speculation, for instance, that poliomyelitis is a comparatively new disease. However, little is as yet known about the procedure whereby a virus "learns" to use man as a host.

Of course, germs do change and from one generation to the next develop new characteristics and new abilities. Some do so more easily and readily than others and present us with diseases that do not confer permanent immunity.

Colds and influenza, for instance, are notorious for their ability to strike again and again. The viruses involved change readily from one generation to the next, these changes being referred to as *mutations*.

Now antibodies to combine with an antigen need to make a good fit. This means they are *specific* and will not combine with an antigen for which they are not designed (just as a key will not fit a lock for which it is not designed). An antibody which will fit a virus perfectly may not fit a mutated virus. For this reason, our antibodies against colds and flu are always failing us.

Sometimes a mutated virus happens to be particularly infectious or has unusually harmful effects. When this happens, there is an *epidemic* as the virus attacks the population, which is unsupplied with antibodies against it. The flu epidemic of 1918 was due to such a mutated virus. So was the less deadly "Asiatic flu" epidemic of 1957.

(The mutations of viruses and bacteria give rise occasionally to a particular variety or *strain* with a body chemistry that makes it indifferent to the presence of a particular antibiotic. The antibiotic kills the unmutated germs, while the *resistant strain* multiplies unchecked. Physicians are therefore constantly plagued with the declining efficiency of their antibiotics and must depend on biochemists to find them new ones. For the same reason, insecticides lose their protency over the years as DDT-resistant flies, for instance, develop.)

Naturally, it would be useful if one didn't have to wait for the body to produce its own antibodies. Why go through a week of sickness and run the risk of death if the germs should get too strong a hold in the interval?

There are some ways out. For instance, people who have recovered from measles possess measles antibody. If such people donate blood, and the gamma-globulin is separated out, a concentrated form of measles antibody exists. Now if a child is exposed to measles, he or she can be given an injection of some of this antibody.

Enough antibody can be given to prevent the measles virus from getting any hold at all. This, as I've explained above, is not entirely good for the host. The foreign antibodies which have been injected into the child's blood stream are eliminated fairly quickly and the body is then just as susceptible to measles as ever.

The ideal case is to give the child enough measles antibody to keep the measles attack mild but not enough to prevent an attack completely. A mild attack will not bother the child, but will allow enough virus into the blood stream to stimulate the child's chemical machinery into forming its own antibodies for future use. The child is then immune to future attacks.

Antibodies can be deliberately formed by using animals. For instance, a horse can be injected with small quantities of the toxin formed by the diphtheria bacillus. The horse forms an antibody (*antitoxin*) neutralizing it. The antitoxin can be obtained by bleeding the horse periodically and isolating the gamma-globulin fraction. Such an antitoxin can then be used to arrest cases of diphtheria in humans.

The best device is always to make the patient form his own antibodies. Sometimes, it is possible to take advantage of the fact that antibody specificity is not perfect.

For instance, Edward Jenner originated *vaccination* against small-pox by deliberately infecting people with a much milder disease called cow-pox. (The virus causing cow-pox is called "vaccinia" from the Latin word for "cow" and from that comes the word "vaccination.") The cow-pox virus does little damage, though its structure is so similar to the small-pox virus that antibodies formed against the former, work also against the latter. Hence people who recovered from the mild cow-pox were immune, thereafter, to the deadly small-pox.

But not every disease has such a convenient little brother. We must learn to create them.

Imagine, for instance, a virus with a spot on its surface to which antibody can be attached (call it the "antibody-spot"). Imagine, too, the presence of a second spot on the surface which plays some essential part in the infectiousness of the virus or in the damage it can do (call it the "danger-spot"). Now the cow-pox virus and the small-pox virus must have had identical "antibody-spots," but different "danger-spots."

Suppose we take a virus, then, and do something to it chemically, which will change the "danger-spot" but not the "antibody spot." In effect, we will be creating a cow-pox type of virus out of a small-pox type.

This has to be done more or less by hit-or-miss. That is, a dangerous virus is treated with this chemical and that in different concentrations for different lengths of time and under different conditions. Each modified virus is then injected into some animal. If the animal does not get the disease, the "danger-spot" has been eliminated. The next question is has the "antibody spot" been eliminated? The animal must be injected with the original virus. If it still does not get the disease, it has developed immunity and the "antibody spot" has not been damaged.

As a result of experiments something like this, Jonas Salk developed a modified virus that does not cause poliomyelitis but produces antibodies that will be effective against the real virus. In this way, the *Salk vaccine* (modified viruses are always called "vaccine" because of the connection with the original cow-pox vaccinia virus) may wipe out poliomyelitis as cow-pox practically wiped out small-pox.

Similarly, a toxin, such as that produced by the tetanus germ may be modified into non-poisonousness, while retaining the ability to stimulate the formation of the proper antibodies. Such modified toxins are called *toxoids*.

So far, the formation of antibodies seems a very useful ability for the body to possess, and so it is. However, the body uses this ability to battle against any foreign protein, even when the foreign protein is not the danger a virus or bacterium is. Sometimes, in fact, the body's defense is a far greater danger than the foreign protein is.

For instance, a foreign protein (harmless in itself) may be injected into the blood stream of an animal and there stimulate the production of antibodies to that protein. The animal becomes *sensitized* to that protein. Under the proper conditions, a second injection of the protein will cause a violent reaction, or even death (*anaphylactic shock*).

This happens occasionally to humans who are receiving injections of some serum developed in animals (as I described in the case of diphtheria antitoxin). Such a serum contains proteins foreign to the body and even though some of them may be most helpful, indeed life-saving, the body nevertheless automatically prepares its defenses. If it becomes too sensitized to those proteins, a future injection may cause fever, rash, itching, all sorts of discomfort. This is *serum sickness*.

Insulin, fortunately, is a protein which is a poor antigen. That is, it does not, generally, stimulate the formation of antibodies. Every once in a while, though, some patient will form antibodies and become sensitive to insulin. This is serious because he must have the insulin to maintain health. The solution, usually, is to switch from insulin obtained from beef pancreas (if that is what he is using) to insulin obtained from hog pancreas. The two insulins are slightly different structurally and though both will work to counteract diabetes equally well, the antibodies to one will not work for the other.

Such troubles, resulting from a defense mechanism "over-defending," so to speak, are minor. Only a small part of the population needs to be injected over and over again with some foreign substance. Surely, the rest of us are safe.

Well, not always. Every one of us runs the risk of becoming sensitized to some foreign protein at some time in our life. Why this should be is not certain.

There is evidence that occasionally proteins which are largely, or even entirely, intact can get across the linings of the mouth and intestines and find their way into the blood stream. There is then the possibility that antibodies may be formed against that protein. Perhaps some people are more easily stimulated to form antibodies against certain proteins so that if milk protein got into the blood in tiny quantities, person A might form antibodies and not person B.

In any case, those unfortunate individuals who do manage to form antibodies against perfectly harmless proteins that may accidentally have found their way, in tiny quantities, into the blood stream, show all sorts of uncomfortable symptoms upon coming into contact with those proteins later on. They develop a running nose, itching, difficulty in breathing, swellings, hives and so on. Different people react in different ways. Such people are exhibiting the effects of an *allergy*.

One common form of allergy is against the pollen of certain plants which, at some times of the year, fill the atmosphere. Such an allergy is commonly called *hay fever*. Allergies to proteins in various foods force the sufferer to choose his diet with care. You might be allergic to cat dandruff and be unable to endure a cat in the same room and have an unfailing nose for distinguishing mink from mink-dyed cat. You may be allergic to your wife's face-powder, so that either powder or wife must be changed.

In fact, the first step in treating an allergy is to determine what it is, exactly, that the patient is allergic to, and sometimes this is the hardest part of the treatment.

In short, although the body in a million ways shows itself to be very "cleverly" run, allergy is one of the most dramatic proofs that the body can also be very "stupid."

Chapter 14

Self-Sealing

BLOOD is unique in being a liquid tissue. That gives it a number of special advantages that have been discussed throughout this book. It also gives it a special disadvantage. It can be spilled.

This is most obvious, and most dangerous, when a large blood-vessel, particularly an artery, is cut. Blood does not merely spill out of a cut artery, it is pushed out with all the force of the pumping heart. To mend matters, the artery must be pinched off, by means of a tourniquet for instance, until the body has time to make an adjustment.

That the body can make an adjustment to bleeding is obvious to us. We are forever cutting, scraping, tearing and otherwise mutilating the skin, with the almost inevitable result that small blood-vessels are broken and blood begins oozing out. Generally, this doesn't worry us. We clean the wound and apply some antiseptic to prevent infection, but we are not concerned about loss of blood. We know, from long experience, that after a while the blood flow will stop and the blood itself thicken or *clot*, that a scab will form over the break in the skin, that eventually the scab will fall off and new and unbroken skin will be exposed.

Actually, the process involves three stages:

(1) When blood-vessels are injured, they first dilate so that blood flows more freely than it would ordinarily. There is active bleeding. This is not as bad as it sounds. In fact, it is

useful since the blood flow helps wash out dirt and micro-organisms that may have entered with whatever blow, scrape or cut that caused the wound.

(2) After a short time, the vessels contract again and the rate of bleeding diminishes. Now the clot has time to form.

(3) About thirty minutes to two hours after this, the vessels again dilate so that more blood enters the area and wound repair can begin. (Some varieties of white blood cells may contribute to this type of repair.) The dilation of the vessels does not mean renewed bleeding, however, since by this time, the clot has blocked off the opening to the outside world.

The blood clot consists mainly of formed elements of the blood entangled in a network of protein fiber. The fiber network makes up only about 1 per cent of the clot, but it is essential to it. Without it, the blood would simply flow indefinitely.

The protein of the fiber network is called *fibrin*. Obviously, there can be no fibrin in circulating blood. If there were, the red cells would be entangled in it and blood movement would be impossible, and so would life. But there must be something in the blood, which on contact with the air or as a result of damage to the blood-vessel, becomes fibrin.

This something is a protein in the blood plasma which is called *fibrinogen* ("giving birth to fibrin"). On electrophoresis, fibrinogen shows up between the beta-globulin and gamma-globulin fractions. Physically, it differs from the other plasma proteins in having a molecule that is particularly long and thin. (Most protein molecules are rather cigar-shaped, but fibrinogen is longer and thinner than any of the others, a "panatella" variety.)

Chemically, though, fibrinogen has a distinguishing feature that is much more important. Under the appropriate circumstances, a small portion of the fibrinogen molecule can be removed. This lost portion, making up less than 1 per cent of the whole, is called *fibrino-peptide*. The loss of fibrino-peptide exposes atom groupings which cause neighboring molecules of fibrinogen to combine firmly. (It is like removing the protective paper layer from a band-aid. The exposed surface is sticky where the original paper was not.) The result of the combination of fibrinogen molecules (almost instantly after the loss of fibrino-peptide) is the formation of an indefinitely long fibrin molecule. It is that molecule which makes up the framework of the clot.

If whole blood is drawn from an animal (or a human) and allowed to stand, it will clot. The fibrinogen will turn to fibrin and enmesh the formed elements. After a while, a straw-colored liquid will separate from the contracting clot. This is ordinary blood plasma with only one thing missing, the fibrinogen. Blood plasma minus fibrinogen is usually referred to as *blood serum*.

Actually, it is rather difficult to work with blood plasma itself since the fibrinogen in it will clot so readily. It is much simpler to let the fibrinogen go and work with the blood serum. It is for this reason that plasma proteins, plasma albumin, plasma globulin and so on are often given the alternative names of *serum proteins*, *serum albumin* and *serum globulin*.

There must be some mechanism whereby fibrinogen can be changed to fibrin quickly when a clot is needed. This is done by means of an enzyme. Fibrinogen will not, of its own accord, lose fibrino-peptide and change to fibrin except at an excessively slow rate. In the presence of some appropriate enzyme, this change is catalyzed and made to proceed quickly. The enzyme involved is called *thrombin,* from a Greek word meaning "clot."

Obviously, when the skin is broken and bleeding begins, thrombin appears from somewhere and the fibrinogen which, until then, had been circulating peacefully in the body, is suddenly converted to fibrin.

The thrombin, I said, "appears from somewhere" simply because it stands to reason that it could not have existed in the blood before the wound. If it did, it would convert fibrinogen to fibrin within the body with fatal results. Obviously, there must be something in the circulating blood which is itself inactive, which has no power to affect fibrinogen, but which at the appropirate moment can be changed to thrombin. We need what scientists call an *inactive precursor*. (Fibrinogen itself is an inactive precursor of fibrin.)

Such an inactive precursor of thrombin is indeed present in the plasma and is called *prothrombin*.

Of course, this only sets the problem one step further back. What converts the prothrombin to thrombin at the crucial moment? One of the substances necessary for this is calcium ion. No other ion will do in its place, but there is no question of substitution. Calcium ion is always present in the plasma, and always at the proper level. (Calcium ion could be imagined to be reduced in quantity in the plasma, but a 10 per cent reduction would be fatal because muscle action, including that of the heart, depends upon it.)

On the other hand, calcium ion by itself is not enough. Something else is needed, a protein called *thromboplastin*. This is an enzyme which catalyzes the removal of a fragment of the prothrombin molecule, converting it to thrombin. The thromboplastin, in other words unmasks the active atom group of thrombin, just as thrombin itself unmasks the active atom groupings of fibrinogen.

This is all very well, but there's a certain feeling of going round and round on a carousel, for it is obvious that thromboplastin can't exist in circulating blood as such, either. If it did, it would change prothrombin to thrombin, thrombin would change fibrinogen to fibrin, and life would be impossible.

So instead, there are a number of inactive precursors of thromboplastin present in blood and in tissues, too. A number of them are required for the formation of thromboplastin and all together they may be lumped under the name of *thromboplastinogen*.

And now we must have something to convert thromboplastinogen to thromboplastin and sometime, somehow we must have the active substance present as such in the blood; otherwise we simply keep stepping further and further back in this eternal merry-go-round.

The merry-go-round ends here, though. The substance that catalyzes the conversion of thromboplastinogen to thromboplastin is present in blood in active form. Then how is clotting prevented in the circulating blood? The converting material is present, but it is safely locked away in tiny containers.

These containers are the third of the three formed elements I mentioned in Chapter 3. They are called *platelets* (because they look like small plates) and *thrombocytes* ("clotting cells"). They are the smallest of the three formed elements, being only 2 to 4 microns in diameter as compared with 7½ microns for the red cells, which are themselves considerably smaller than ordinary cells.

The platelets are not cells, of course; even less so than the red cells. They are formed in bone marrow (as red cells are) from special large cells called *megakaryocytes*. A week after formation, a megakaryocyte will develop graininess in its cytoplasm and then falls apart into small pieces—the platelets. The lifetime of the platelets, as determined from isotoype studies, is from 8 to 10 days in man.

This, then, is the completed chain. As the result of a wound, blood oozes out into the open air. The platelets, which are quite fragile (and of which 250,000 are present in each millimeter of blood), break. The material within converts thromboplastinogen to thromboplastin; the thromboplastin plus calcium ion converts prothrombin to thrombin; the thrombin converts fibrinogen to fibrin; and the clot forms. This seems a rather long and roundabout way of arranging to have the blood clot, and biochemists, in fact, are continually finding new complications. It has gotten so that they simply speak of *clotting factors* and number them by Roman numerals. The substances I've already mentioned are the main factors. Thus, fibrinogen is *clotting factor I,* prothrombin is *clotting factor II,* thromboplastin is *clotting factor III* and calcium ion is *clotting factor IV*. In addition, however, there are various proteins found among the plasma globulins which are members of the thromboplastinogen group, or help accelerate one step or another and so on. There are at least ten factors numbered now and possibly there will be more by the time this book comes out.

As for the reason for the complications in the chain (unless it is to irritate biochemists), this is not clear. It's obvious, though, that the blood has a hard task; it must have the capacity to form clots at a moment's notice when exposed to air, and yet not be so sensitive a clot former as to form clots within the body.

Obviously, if the platelets are fragile enough to burst on mere exposure to air, they can't survive repeated buffetings against the walls of blood-vessels. (As a matter of fact the lifespan of the average platelet is thought not to be more than three to five days.) Somehow the complicated chain involved in clotting must make it possible for the body to avoid accidents such as broken platelets within the body. Exactly how we do not know, but we do know that clots do occasionally form within the blood-vessels, especially when the walls are rough, as in atherosclerosis, and, presumably, platelets are more easily broken against them. This does not happen often and it must be the mechanism of the clotting chain that keeps it from happening more often.

Of course, the deficiency or outright absence of any of these clotting factors will interrupt the chain and result in extended or even continuous bleeding from a wound. For instance, it occasionally happens that a human being is born with a deficiency of fibrinogen or prothrombin. In this case, the *clotting time* is prolonged, sometimes, to a dangerous point. Since fibrinogen is formed in the liver, severe liver disorders may result in low fibrinogen in the blood and a consequent tendency to hemorrhage. In some cases, the platelets are low in number (either from birth or as a result of being crowded out by swarming leukocytes in leukemia) or, what is just as bad, insufficiently fragile so that few break on exposure to air. Again, clotting is delayed.

The best known of the bleeding diseases is, however, *hemophilia* (from Greek words meaning "love of blood"). A hemophiliac will bleed indefinitely from even minor wounds and is in danger of death from a scratch, while a tooth extraction is a major operation that must not be entered into without the gravest preparation.

Hemophilia is the result of an inherited inability on the part of the body to form *antihemophilic globulin*, which is also called *clotting factor VIII*. This is one of the major thromboplastinogen components. Without it, even if the platelets break, there is nothing for them to work on.

Failure of other of the thromboplastinogen components produce diseases very like hemophilia in character. In fact, a whole family of *hemophilioid states* is now recognized. Ordinary hemophilia (also called "classical hemophilia") is now called *hemophilia A*. Another comparatively well-studied variety is *hemophilia B*, which results from a congential deficiency of *clotting factor IX*.

The proper name of this factor is *plasma thromboplastic component*, often abbreviated as *PTC*. It occurs in the beta₂-globulin fraction of the plasma proteins.

By an odd turn of events, the first case of hemophilia B to be thoroughly studied was found in a young boy whose last name happened to be Christmas. With a peculiar lack of sensitivity, physicians took to calling this condition *Christmas disease* as a result, a name which is catching on, while PTC is often called *Christmas factor*.

Hemophilia is inherited in an unusual manner, which involves a difference between the sexes and which will require a bit of explanation.

In Chapter 6, I discussed the inheritance of the blood group substances and described how a child obtained its genes from both parents. There are some cases, however, in which a particular gene is inherited from the mother only, and that comes about in the following way.

The genes in the cells of the human body are grouped into chains. Each chain of genes forms a structure called a *chromosome* (which will absorb certain dyes strongly and which can thus be made visible to the naked eye, so that it may be intensively studied).

These chromosomes occur in pairs. Each chromosome of a particular pair contains genes for a series of identical characteristics. Thus, if a gene in a particular position on one chromosome of a pair governs the inheritance of eye-color, so does the gene in that position on the other chromosome of the pair. The genes themselves may not be identical—one may tend to produce brown eyes and one blue eyes—but both are concerned with the same characteristic, eye-color in this case.

Thus, every gene (with certain exceptions I'll soon come to) would seem to have a spare. This is most useful. If, for some reason, a particular gene is defective, the chances are that its paired gene is normal and, in most cases, the body can make do well enough on the single normal gene.

In forming the sex cells, the pairs of chromosomes separate. The male sperm cell contains only one chromosome of each pair in the male cells generally. The female egg cell also contains only one chromosome of each pair in the female cells generally. When sperm and egg combine to form the fertilized ovum, there is present once again the full complement of pairs. One of each pair, however, has been derived from the mother and one from the father.

The result of such a mixing of genes in each generation has been described in Chapter 6 as far as blood group substances are concerned. As it is for those, so it is for most other human characteristics that are gene-controlled.

But there is one important difference between the sexes as far as chromosomes are concerned. The cells of a human female contain twenty-three pairs of chromosomes. (Until 1957, it was generally believed that there were twenty-four pairs, but a more careful count by Japanese scientists in that year showed that it was twenty-three in the majority of cases.)

The cells of the human male also contain twenty-three pairs, but of these one pair consists of two widely different chromosomes. The twenty-third pair consists of one normal chromosome and one stub of a chromosome that contains no genes. The normal twenty-third chromosome is called an *X-chromosome*. The stub is called a *Y-chromosome*. Thus, female cells contain two X-chromosomes, while male cells contain an X-chromosome and a Y-chromosome.

Observe the results in the formation of sex cells. When a female produces egg cells, each individual egg cell contains one of each pair of chromosomes. Each contains the full complement of twenty-three chromosomes, including one X-chromosome.

This is not true of the sperm cells produced by the male. When the chromosome pairs of the male divide up, one individual set is made up of twenty-three normal chromosomes, including the X-chromosome. The other is made up of twenty-two normal chromosomes plus the worthless Y-chromosome. Half the sperm cells formed by the male contain one set, half the other. So there are two kinds of sperm cells which we might call "X-sperm" and "Y-sperm." Naturally, there are equal quantities of each, since half get one of each pair and half the other.

In the process of fertilization, the chances that an egg cell will be fertilized by an X-sperm are roughly equal to those that it will be fertilized by a Y-sperm. (Actually, the Y-sperm, containing twenty-two chromosomes plus a stub, is a trifle lighter than the X-sperm, with twenty-three full-sized chromosomes, can swim a trifle faster and can get to the waiting egg cell a trifle more quickly. For that reason, Y-sperm fertilizations occur a bit more often than X-sperm fertilizations.)

An X-sperm fertilization results in a fertilized ovum with two X-chromosomes. Such an ovum must develop into a female. A Y-sperm fertilization results in a fertilized ovum with one X-chromosome and one Y-chromosome, and this must develop into a male. (The equal chances of the two fertilizations account for the fact that the number of girl babies and boy babies are roughly equal, with a small edge in favor of boys because of the lightness of the Y-sperm.)

Now if a gene in an egg cell (or sperm cell) is defective,

the corresponding gene in the sperm cell (or the egg cell) is probably all right and the child is usually born without serious defect in that particular characteristic.

The only exception to this general rule occurs when the defective gene occurs in the X-chromosome. Let's call such a gene an X-defective. Suppose a mother has an X-defective and a normal gene (an X-normal) as the pair. Half the egg cells she produces have only an X-defective, the other half have only the X-normal.

The X-normal egg cells, once fertilized, are perfectly all right and we need consider them no further. The X-defective egg cells may be fertilized in two ways. If the fertilization is by way of an X-sperm, the gene in the X-sperm is probably normal and the fertilized ovum contains an X-defective and an X-normal. The girl baby that results (it must be a girl since there are two X-genes) is therefore usually without serious defect in that particular characteristic. However, since she does contain the X-defect she can still carry it on to future generations. She is a *carrier*.

The chances that a particular daughter will be a carrier like her mother are 50-50. This does not mean that if an X-defective mother has two daughters, one must be a carrier and one not. It just means that that particular situation is somewhat more likely than that both should be carriers or both not. An X-defective mother may have ten daughters, all defective, or all normal (though the chances of that, assuming the ten daughters to begin with, are only 1 in 1024).

But what of an X-defective egg cell which is fertilized by a Y-sperm? There is no gene in the Y-chromosome to balance the X-defective. The boy baby that results (it must be a boy since there is only one X-gene) is born with a defect.

The chances that a particular son of such a woman should be born with a defect are again 50-50. After all, she could have a son as a result of a Y-sperm fertilization of an X-normal egg cell and half the egg cells she produces are X-normal. She might have ten sons, all of whom are normal, or all defective, though again the chances of such a situation, assuming the ten sons, are only 1 in 1024.

To the casual observer, however, who isn't worried about genes and chromosomes, it will simply appear that a mother (who shows no signs of any defect in a particular characteristic) will have daughters, all of whom show no signs of it, and sons, some of whom do. Only the sons seem to be affected.

Such a human characteristic which is defective on occasion, but only in one sex (usually the male), is called a *sex-linked characteristic*.

Suppose now an X-defective male marries a normal female. All the egg cells produced by the mother are, of course, X-normal. There are two types of sperm cells, however, an X-defective sperm and a Y-sperm. If an X-defective sperm fertilizes an X-normal egg, the result is a girl who shows no effect but is a carrier. If a Y-sperm fertilizes the X-normal egg, the result is a normal boy who, since he obtains no X-defective gene at all, is not even a carrier.

To summarize. In such a sex-linked characteristic, a male may show a defect but will not have defective children; while a female may not show a defect and yet have defective children. (Of course, if an X-defective male marries a girl who is a carrier, a fertilized ovum may end up with two X-defective genes, so that a defective female will result. This happens exceedingly rarely.)

The fact that males are not protected against defects among the genes in the X-chromosomes mean that males, generally, are more subject to imperfections than are females. Some of these imperfections are large enough to be noticeable. Others are so small as not to be detectable by modern techniques, and yet they may take their toll in the long run.

It is probably because of these imperfections, large and small, that though more male children are conceived (because the Y-sperm travels a bit faster than the X-sperm), more males than females are still-born, more males than females die in the first year and in every year thereafter, so that, on the whole, the life-expectancy of the female in the United States is at least three years longer than that of the male.

To get back to the original subject, hemophilia is an example of a sex-linked characteristic. The actual sufferers are almost invariably males; the carriers are always females.

Hemophilia in the twentieth century received a great deal of publicity because it cropped up in two different royal families. The Tsarevitch Alexis, only son of Tsar Nicholas II, was born in 1904 with hemophilia. This had an important effect on history. The "mad monk," Gregory Rasputin, had the ability to stop Alexis's bleeding by some sort of hypnotic mumbo-jumbo, after the doctors had failed. At least, Tsarina Alexandra, Alexis's mother, believed Rasputin could do this.

This gave Rasputin great influence at court and, since he was an unsavory character, this created scandal, added to corruption and intrigue, and played a significant part in bringing about the Russian Revolution.

A few years after the birth of Alexis, a hemophiliac son was also born to the Spanish king, Alfonxo XIII.

Now there are no records of hemophiliacs previously in either royal family (and royal genealogies are kept almost as carefully as are those of thoroughbred horses). Apparently, it arose because an X-normal gene had in one of its numerous duplications and reduplications (every time a new cell is formed a new gene must be synthesized) allowed an imperfection to creep in, so that an X-defective resulted. In other words, it arose through a mutation. These things happen all the time, as for instance in the development of defective genes that result in the formation of abnormal hemoglobins (see Chapter 7).

It is, however, highly unlikely that two mutations of the same dramatic sort would occur in two royal families at the same time. It seems much more likely that the mutation occurred at some point from which the two families branched off; and moreover at some point in the not too distant past as otherwise it would have showed up sooner.

Since a sex-linked characteristic like hemophilia is transmitted only by females, we must concentrate on the mothers involved. The mother of the Tsarevitch was Alexandra of Hesse-Darmstadt, the daughter of Alice, second daughter of Queen Victoria of England. The mother of the Spanish prince was Victoria of Battenberg, daughter of Beatrice, youngest daughter of Queen Victoria of England.

The two royal families, then, join by way of the female line at no less a person than Queen Victoria. Now Queen Victoria had only non-hemophiliac sons (with the possible exception of one who died in infancy and who might, for all we know, have been afflicted), who, of course, have only non-hemophiliac descendants. Still, this does not mean that the Queen was not a carrier. A carrier with three sons has a 1 in 8 chance of having all three normal and Victoria was lucky.

It seems certain, though, that Queen Victoria bore at least two daughters who were hemophilia carriers and either they developed the mutation independently or, and this is much more likely, they inherited it from their mother, or, of course, just possibly from Queen Victoria's mother.

For a while, because of all this, it was fashionable to call hemophilia the "royal disease"; at least it was fashionable among the sob-sisters of the tabloid press. There was no justification for this, of course. Uncounted thousands of commoners have had hemophilia, whereas it afflicted royalty for only twenty-eight years from 1904, when Alexis was born, to 1931, when the Spanish royal family followed the Russian royal family into non-royalty and oblivion. There are other conditions which have afflicted European royalty much longer and much more frequently than hemophilia has, and which have a much better right to be called the "royal disease." Insanity, for instance.

There are times when clotting can be a serious nuisance. During operations, for instance, the formation of clots at the point where the surgeon is working is an annoying complication. Fortunately, there exist anti-clotting substances. The body itself produces a substance called *heparin*. It is distributed throughout the body, but is most concentrated in the liver and lungs. (In fact, the word "heparin" is derived from the Greek word for "liver.")

Heparin halts clotting altogether by interfering with the chain of events at three points at least. No doubt, the body uses it as one of its safeguards against internal clotting. And the surgeon can use it for similar purposes. A bit of purified heparin added at the point of operation will render the blood temporarily incoagulable. The surgeon can work.

The leech, a blood-sucking animal, contains a similar anti-clotting substance, one called *hirudin*, which it uses for offense rather than defense. At least, it injects this while he is busy sucking blood, since obviously the formation of blood clots would interfere with its meal. No doubt other blood-feeders engage in similar tricks.

Clotting can also be prevented by interfering with a particular vitamin. This is vitamin K which, for some reason not quite understood, is essential to clotting. The best guess, so far, is that it may be necessary for the production of pro-thrombin by the liver and that without it prothrombin is in too short supply for clotting. (The K in vitamin K stands for *Koagulation*, the German word for "clotting.")

Now ordinarily, there is no problem involving vitamin K. It is formed by the bacteria in our intestines, so that generally we have an adequate supply regardless of the nature of our diet. However, there is one group of human beings that lack intestinal bacteria and that group consists of new-born babies, who are born bacteria-free.

In old days before modern notions of hygiene and antiseptic conditions came in, this wasn't serious. Germs so swarmed that the new-born child picked up his own supply almost at once.

Nowadays, however, hospitals are so clean and infants are kept so purely sterilized that it takes some three days for bacteria to gain a foothold. For those three days, there is a chance that the infant will have serious trouble if, for any reason, he starts to bleed. He is a temporory hemophiliac, in other words. Well, there's no use in abandoning cleanliness—too many dangers are introduced—so instead the child is routinely given a vitamin K injection after birth. Or, as an alternative, the mother may be given a good dose just before the child is born, in which case enough leaks across the placenta into the child's blood stream to protect it.

There is a compound which resembles vitamin K sufficiently to interfere with its workings. The liver enzymes that form prothrombin and that use vitamin K in the process will pick up this other compound instead and find themselves occupied and helpless. This interfering compound is called *dicumarol* and is found in spoiled hay. Cattle, eating such hay, suffer a shortage of prothrombin (*hypoprothrombinemia*) and develop bleeding which can be fatal.

Since human beings don't eat hay, spoiled or otherwise, dicumarol is not a danger to us. In fact, it can be a help. Unlike heparin it does not work at once, so that it is useless in emergencies as, for instance, during the actual course of an operation. However, it has a slow action that begins about twenty-four hours after injection and then continues for quite a while. If given to a patient following an operation, it gives him a temporarily hard-to-clot blood. The value of that is that it prevents internal clotting at those points where blood-vessels were inevitably damaged during the operation. This obviously helps preserve life.

Another time during which blood clotting is definitely not desired is when blood is collected for use in later transfusions. Clotted blood cannot be transfused.

There is a simple way of taking care of this. The vessel in which blood is collected contains a dilute, sterile solution of a citrate or an oxalate. Either citrate ion or oxalate ion will combine tightly with almost every calcium ion in sight. Once the calcium ion of the blood is thus tied up, clotting is impossible. Calcium ion is clotting factor IV and is essential, as I have said, in the conversion of prothrombin to thrombin. Without that step the chain of the clotting mechanism is broken.

It is by this simple device that blood can be collected and kept liquid for use.

If you have ever donated blood you have watched it trickle into such a vessel and you may have looked at it curiously afterward—a dark red liquid, which you yourself have produced and which may mean the difference between life and death for another person. It is being kept liquid for use and in the veins of another it will take on all the duties it is so capable of performing.

For blood, as Goethe said in the quotation I gave at the beginning of the book, is quite a special fluid.

It is the indefatigable transit system of the body, with special tricks for carrying oxygen from lungs to cells, and carbon dioxide from cells to lungs; for carrying nitrogen wastes to the kidneys and the products of digestion to the liver; for carrying sugars, lipids and proteins to all cells; for carrying ions, hormones and vitamins wherever needed; for distributing heat where necessary; for bringing the battle reserves to the point of the outside invasion dangers. And to top it all off, it is self-sealing and plugs its own leaks.

It is difficult to imagine a fluid so versatile and so useful; one that has so many widely diverse duties to perform; and one that performs them all so well.

Next time you donate blood, or, for that matter, next time you scratch yourself and draw blood, take another look at the red fluid. It's worth another look. There's nothing else in the world like it.

INDEX

The body's transit system

The bloodstream, in Isaac Asimov's words, is the indefatigable transit system of the body, with special tricks for carrying oxygen from lungs to cells and carbon dioxide from cells to lungs; for carrying nitrogen wastes to the kidneys and the products of digestion to the liver; for carrying sugars, lipids, and proteins to all cells; or carrying ions, hormones and vitamins wherever needed; for distributing heat where necessary; for bringing the battle reserves to the point of the outside invasion dangers. And to top it all off, it is self-sealing and plugs its own leaks.

It is difficult to imagine a fluid so versatile and so useful—one that has so many widely diverse duties to perform and performs them all so well. In The Bloodstream Dr. Asimov details step by step the manifold activities of blood and the marvels it performs.

Isaac Asimov, Associate Professor of Biochemistry at Boston University School of Medicine, has gained international distinction as both a science writer and a writer of science fiction. His many works include The World of Carbon, The Clock We Live On, Marvels of Science, The Kingdom of the Sun, The World of Nitrogen, and Fifty Short Science Fiction Tales, all available in Collier Books.

Cover Design: Kenneth R. Deardoff

COLLIER BOOKS

866 THIRD AVENUE, NEW YORK, N.Y. 10022